CONF

OF A

HIGH-PRICED CALL GIRL

Dimitra Ekmektsis

Andrews UK Limited

Copyright © 2010, 2012 Dimitra Ekmektsis

This edition published in 2012 by
Andrews UK Limited
The Hat Factory
Luton, LU1 2EY
www.andrewsuk.com

This book is sold subject to the condition that it shall not, by
way of trade or otherwise, be lent, resold, hired out or otherwise
circulated without the publisher's prior written consent in any
form of binding or cover other than that in which it is published,
and without a similar condition being imposed on the subsequent
purchaser.

The right of Dimitra Ekmektsis to be identified as author of this
book has been asserted in accordance with section 77 and 78 of
the Copyrights Designs and Patents Act 1988.

Contents

Contents

My grandparents, Eleftheria and Ioannis Gialampoukis, have given me many gifts of incalculable value. However, the greatest gift they have given me has been the love and appreciation of writing. It is impossible for me to adequately express my gratitude to them, and I will never be able to repay them for what they have given me. With the deepest love and respect, I offer this book as a tribute to them.

Prologue

In times immemorial, beautiful women were brought to temples in hopes of being educated as priestesses. They were sacred prostitutes. The priestesses received the strangers who came to the temples, and their sexual union was, for both participants, communion with the goddess of love and fertility.

Both the act of lovemaking and the payment were dedicated to the goddess and thus made holy. The sexual union was between goddess and god, and the human counterparts who played the roles assumed divine status during the act. These rituals were believed to bring prosperity to the land and to the people.

Chapter One

I am a call girl. I provide human companionship and pleasure.

I like providing this pleasure, and I hope by reading my story you will come to understand me better and be further intrigued by the person I am.

The memoirs of call girls are much in demand these days – a millennial craze. It seems that every call girl wants to write her story, but it is actually quite difficult. You wouldn't believe the dedication it takes to record your clandestine encounters with wealthy men from around the globe. These men pay fabulously for a woman's companionship, be it for one hour, an evening, a weekend, or more.

Men often feel bitterly oppressed by the role they have to play every day, the expectation that they be rational and responsible. Call girls offer an escape and refuge from the limitations of life and the monotony of marriage, even if only for a few hours. I am a professional girlfriend, if you will, and I prefer to think of the time I spend with clients as dates and treat them as dates (or boyfriends).

You have to possess a great deal of empathy to be a call girl. I sometimes see myself as a psychoanalyst. Most of my clients are repeats, and they tell me a lot about their personal lives and problems.

I have forged some amazing friendships through this business. I correspond with authors, journalists, and even film producers, all of whom regard me as their muse.

My selling point is my intellect – it is essential to be able to converse with clients on their level: I speak three languages fluently and have a wide variety of passions to bring to the table.

I like to research a client's interests before I meet him. I was born to be playful and sweet and so, typically, my clients treat me with warmth and respect. If the right chemistry is not there, then

I don't bother. Luckily, the demand for call girls is always higher than the supply.

The getting-paid-for-companionship subject was brought to the fore when *The Happy Hooker* hit the bookshelves. An icon to many who have followed in her footsteps, the author, Xaviera Hollander, opened my eyes to an atypical career path when I was only twelve years old.

The blonde Dutch beauty, Xaviera had been at the center of a great international sex scandal involving the United Nations in New York, as well as the administration in Washington D.C.

Miss Hollander, it was revealed, had provided the services of herself and other women for the intimate, private pleasures of powerful men, including business magnates, diplomats, and foreign officials. I pored through this best-selling book, fascinated by her exciting life and unimaginable happenings but not understanding a word.

Xaviera told of mobsters, lesbianism, bondage, and run-ins with the FBI. In awe, my pre-teen self-came to the conclusion that I could do the very same, should I wish to.

And so it happened, by shocking the world Xaviera Hollander was transformed into the latest overnight celebrity. She wrote eighteen books, as well as a monthly sex advice column for *Penthouse* magazine. She is still a well-recognized name today.

Inevitably, all call girls – certainly the ones I've discussed the matter with – worship her. Those of us in the profession agree she is smart, beautiful, honest, and very brave. She is proud of the career she has chosen and has few regrets. Even call girls new to the profession talk and gossip about Xaviera, as well as those of us who have followed her path relentlessly.

Every time I browse the Internet, I stumble upon a new book or blog or HBO special by or about call girls. Whether by word of mouth or via the Internet, gossip is undoubtedly the best source of information about call girls.

I've even been privy to whispering winds regarding my own exploits through this electronic source of gossip collaborated by many. According to the celebrity grapevine, I am this shapely, long-legged party girl with fiery red hair who carried on a risqué, champagne-and-drug-soaked $2,000-a-night affair with Oscar winning screenwriter and producer Aaron Sorkin. Among his many works, he is known for creating the fictitious White House drama *The West Wing*.

I smile knowing that much I hear of myself is true. However, I never admit this to a soul, but my hair is not really red, it is dark blonde. And what many news-spreaders don't know is that, rather than living in a bath of flowing champagne and drugs, I live and work in Reno in the dry, harsh Nevada desert.

But here in this small town community, there are plenty of upsides. For instance, I never have to sit around in traffic during rush hour, and I am certainly not chained to a cubicle in a nine-to-five career. I recall visiting a so-called straight woman once who worked in such a tiny, carpeted-wall prison that I suffered claustrophobia for days afterwards.

The downside of living here is that sometimes you have to keep your profession a secret. Believe me, when you are a call girl and your landlord asks you what you do for work, it pays to quickly to come up with a respectable line. This is especially true if you have developed an undying crush, such as the one I have on my landlord. I told him that I write articles for magazines.

Actually, I *am* a writer, though I don't tell too many people about my almost-secret writing career. The ones to whom I do mention it think the idea of my being an author is awesome.

They imagine that writing about being a call girl is steeped in glamour and intrigue. But, truthfully, writing about my call girl profession, combined with my actual call girl duties, is completely draining. Usually, when I tell people that I'm writing my story, they say, "Wow, how exciting!" My friends, the ones who think they may be noted on the written page, get *really* excited about my writing.

Especially my friend Amber. Amber is a call girl and advertises on the Internet, like me. I consider myself beyond lucky to know her. She is very funny and rather clever.

I recently entered a real estate office while going about the tiring task of apartment hunting. My cell phone rang. It was Amber.

"You need a blog!" Amber was shouting. She didn't even pause to breathe.

"Universal Pictures just made a deal with Aaron Sorkin. He's going to direct Tom Hanks in that movie *Charlie Wilson's War*."

I giggled, and then finally getting a word in, I asked suspiciously, "Have you been Googling Sorkin again?"

"Yes. I have. I have."

Every time Amber googles Aaron, she tells me that I need a blog. In fact, Amber is always after me to get a blog so that I can write on the Internet about my independent call girl business and my distinctive and quite unusual encounters.

"I mean, everybody would read you," she says.

Amber's behavior wasn't at all unusual. Because everyone googles everyone they know. It just sort-of slowly creeps up on you. Before you know it, you even google yourself. I guess we feel that if we don't get googled, our whole world will fall apart.

Before I finish telling you the story of my apartment hunt and about Amber's obsession with my getting a blog, let me tell you a bit about myself.

One. I don't see being a call girl as inherently more exploitative than any other type of work. I always believed that everyone prostitutes some aspect of their body or soul for material gains. "All paid jobs absorb and degrade the mind," said the Greek philosopher Aristotle. Personally, I think that many Hollywood starlets dress like prostitutes, but there is a certain animosity towards call girls, maybe because call girls take some power away from other women. I don't think that most women want men to be able to simply go out and buy sex.

It is difficult for me to understand why it is that a wife trading sex for financial support is granted society's approval. On the other hand, a hard-working call girl is labeled a criminal.

First of all, the reason for this double standard is that sexual exclusivity was codified into Jewish law to protect the church and man's property. Included in "man's property" was his wife. Later, Jewish law became "God's law" and was quickly absorbed into Christianity and then into civil law. The difference between a call girl and a wife is that a call girl provides sex to more than one man, but for a wife to do that would be sinful because she would no longer be a "man's property."

If we lived in a world where every man could get all the sex and love he needs at home, there probably wouldn't be any call girls. But we don't live in that type of society, I'm afraid.

Two. I was born in Greece and grew up in Germany. If some of my clients reveal that they have a weakness for European women, it is, they theorize, because I remind them of what their great-great-great-grandparents might have gone through when they first arrived in America. I am stunned by being compared to these far-removed pilgrims, but I try not to let on and just smile sweetly.

Three. I'm in my thirties. But no one would know if I didn't tell. I still have the shape of a twenty-something. By looking at my lithe body, some think I could be a dancer. But then, others don't grasp the possibilities, like Amber, for instance. When I told Amber about my daily yoga class, she said, "You're crazy. Why would you bother?"

But I just love yoga and fall into the routine like clockwork. I just can't help myself. Also, many think that someone who is as obsessed with books and writing as I am should perhaps be a librarian.

Look, the only way men are going to pay $400 per hour for my company is if I look flawless in lingerie from every angle. Having a mind doesn't really hinder, either.

Four. You wouldn't believe how many men pay call girls. (I'll tell you of some of these men and the experiences I've had with them as I go along.) Some men see call girls all the time. I happen to know that most of these men are lonely and between wives or girlfriends. Of course, sometimes they're just out of town and lonely.

And believe me, even successful and attractive men pay big money to be with a call girl. Please don't tell anyone, because you know some women get so jealous, but many of my clients could go into a bar and pretty easily get a woman to go home with them.

So you may say, "Isn't paying for sex a bit stupid when you can get it for free?" But there is something really intelligent about this form of stupidity. Men who pay call girls usually get transported to a place where they feel special and understood. Where reality is replaced with a warmer light. Where every fantasy can be fulfilled! Not all women are that liberal.

All the clever men who pick up women at bars and give their money to the bartender instead of the woman get hours and hours of drinking and talking. And by then the woman is so drunk, the "free" sex isn't enjoyable anymore.

Five. I am not a drug addict. Some call girls may be drug addicts, but apparently so are some lawyers and accountants.

Six. I am not a victim of childhood sexual abuse, and I don't suffer from low self-esteem. I always say, "Getting rewarded for being physically attractive is not an obvious barrier to self-esteem."

I stepped into Vincent's office and nearly lost my cool. This man, I easily observed, was what I can only describe as delicious. He was sitting behind a desk that was so big it could have easily doubled as a bed. I honestly stared at this heavenly creature. He was arguing with someone on the phone.

I don't know if he paid any attention to me or not, but soon I found myself wondering whether I should tell him that I wanted to do all sorts of shameless things with him. Everything about him was sexy, even the way he argued.

"I've got to go now, Amber," I said, almost in a whisper, and cut her off mid-sentence.

She was talking about Sorkin and all the attention I could get by writing about him on the blog she was proposing I obtain. When I finally hung up my cell phone, I walked over to the hottie at the big, bed-like desk.

Vincent, a striking Italian with longish dark blonde hair and a narrow build, looked exactly like Ed Burns did when he starred in *15 Minutes*. He didn't appear very tall, maybe 5'8", thus proving that good things come in small packages.

"Hi," I said, unconsciously biting my lip.

"Oh hi," he replied. "Can I help you?"

He glanced at me, and I found myself thinking what a shame that I'd dressed to downplay my sexuality in black skinny pants and a long black sweater. It's one thing getting dressed up for a client, but I get paid to look like the woman in the perfume ad. I don't see the need to dress up for everyday tasks.

"Kim from the casino said you could show me some apartments," I managed to say.

"Yes," he said. "I have many great properties available. The best. How much are you looking to spend?" My main concern wasn't money. It was that I couldn't pay attention to the conversation at all. I felt as if I were two feet from Ed Burns.

Vincent didn't wait for me to answer.

"Maybe I can show you some properties, and you can see for yourself," he said.

In less than three minutes, I had fallen for him. Can I tell you a secret? I've never met a man who didn't proposition me for sex very soon after meeting me – and Vincent would be no different from the others, I told myself, as I followed him from the office to his black Hummer in the parking lot. I don't consider myself a supermodel, but I know I'm very attractive, with memorable features; and if I were a man, I would be all over me.

I sat in the passenger seat only inches from Ed Burns, feeling decidedly weak in the knees. While Vincent drove down Lake Street, I wondered what his chest looked like underneath his shirt and, would you believe, I was dying to know the kind of underwear he was wearing – if any. I was waiting for him to lay on a pick-up line, like all the other men do, but Vincent said nothing. He was professional, which was unbearable. Why does the one guy I find unbelievably sexy in I don't know how long have to be the one to play it cool?

I found it extremely hard to focus on renting an apartment. Sometimes I wish there were no Ed Burns-type men in the world, because then I'd never have to worry about getting attention deficit disorder.

Vincent turned onto South Wells Avenue and merged onto Interstate 80 toward Sparks. After about two miles, he exited on Rock Boulevard and turned right onto Victorian Avenue.

Finally, he spoke. "Where do you work?"

"I write magazine articles," I said.

"About what?" he asked, sounding intrigued.

"About...Hollywood," I replied.

He frowned. His cell phone rang, and he answered it. Again, he argued with somebody over business, it seemed. *He's just like me,* I thought. Money on his mind! How hot of him.

He drove the SUV behind a yellow, three-story faux Victorian building and stopped. I followed him inside the lovely structure, and he unlocked the first door on the right.

Ah, I thought instantly, realizing how amazingly convenient this would be for my clients to come straight in without being seen by the neighbors. Inside the one-bedroom apartment, I saw the wonderfully large windows I adore and shiny hardwood floors. It wasn't very big, but that didn't really bother me. I don't need an oversize apartment to write about the various aspects of being a call girl and things most people know nothing about.

Once I'd finished my book, I could live somewhere beautiful like Marbella, exactly like Xaviera Hollander. With this thought, I asked Vincent how much the rent was. (Please don't tell a soul this, but all call girls make more money than most people. Most people find out I'm a call girl after learning that I make lots of money.) Now, here I was with the man I'd just fallen head over heels for, and I really didn't want him to know my profession.

Not yet. Maybe never.

"Six hundred a month," he said. "Do you like it?"

"I do," I said. "But it does need some TLC."

9

It turned out there was a very good reason the rent at the Victorian was so cheap. Someone on my floor smoked so much weed that the hallways reeked with the smell. Sometimes the smell crept into my apartment through the vents. On the third day, I still couldn't figure out which apartment it was coming from.

Though I'd smoked weed for years when I was a dancer in Miami, and later, at the Kit Kat ranch in Carson City, I had quit when I decided to pour my heart into writing. I wasn't a pothead now, and I really didn't want clients thinking that I was.

The truth is, I am all for the legalization of marijuana. I think people should be allowed to smoke weed, just as they are allowed to drink alcohol – but in private, without the entire building reeking. And though Jake, a regular client I had scheduled on this certain evening, was nobody special to me, I didn't want it getting around that I used any kind of drugs, as social as it might be. The closer it got to his arrival time, the more worried I became.

I called Amber. "Hey, it's me."

Amber is in her mid-twenties and has fantastic bone-structure. She resembles Grace Kelly if she'd been a brunette.

"I'm in my new apartment," I said. "It's really weird. My neighbors smoke pot all day long, and I have to meet a client this evening. Can you come over?"

Forty-five minutes later, we were sitting in my small kitchen drinking an Irish coffee. Amber is super-cool, always. This day, she was dressed for the chilly November afternoon in a long green camouflage skirt, black faux fur jacket, and boots. She was playing with my cat, Kenny, who was perched on the table between us, clearly loving the attention.

"You're crazy," Amber said. "Why do you care if your neighbors smoke weed?"

"Because! I don't want my clients to think I'm a pothead and then not take me seriously. And, you know, the smell of weed gives me the munchies. Now I'm going to gain weight."

"But Dimitra, you don't want them to take you too seriously. If they want serious, they can stay home with their wives. You want their money. Period. You've got to stop worrying. Now, tell me about the book. Am I going to be in it?"

"Amber, you know you are," I said.

"That's neat."

Amber and I have a bit more history than most call girls here in Reno. We have both been involved in sex scandals. Clearly, hers was more of the grisly kind.

She had been attacked and nearly killed by a murderer who posed as a client in San Francisco. She had been smart to pretend to be dead. It was only then that he stopped beating her and disposed of her in the San Francisco Bay. She was unrecognizable in the police photographs taken after she managed to swim to the Pier and call 911.

After Amber's assailant was caught, he testified that he had tried to kill her because she was a sinner and therefore didn't deserve to live.

Call girls can be the most vulnerable of all women, sometimes. The unhealthiest thing about the job is the stigma that's attached to it, and many of us suffer terribly from the discrimination and poor treatment we receive from people who accuse us of acting immorally. Fear and depression become job hazards. I have heard stories of call girls who would not go to the police even though they had been beaten and raped. Some were beaten and raped by police because the police view them as immoral.

Allowing people to denounce this major money-earning position on the grounds that most people find it immoral is only encouraging the stigma. I honestly question whether it is most people or just a few making a lot of noise.

In most heterosexual unions, the man is typically physically stronger, with the woman being the receiver during the act of intercourse.

On the other hand, most men who pay for sex are not usually the aggressive type. A man who buys sex usually acts as if asking for a favor, and most call girls practice controlled sex. We decide who gets it, when, for how long, and in what position. At the Kit Kat ranch or other brothels, for example, a man acting in an overly aggressive manner would have to answer to brothel security or to the police. This is why we need legal sex work. Decriminalizing sex work is the first step in removing the stigma.

Getting back to my friend and the abuse she suffered. She was a hot item for the talk shows. Hosts went ape for her to talk about the incident. She was a guest on several of them. After all, she was the only known survivor of that particular serial murderer.

To this day, she suffers from severe post-traumatic stress disorder, and whenever she is alone, she gets flashbacks of her assault.

Amber truly amazes me. I told her I probably wouldn't have had the courage to fake my own death and survive the way she had.

But she realized that was the only thing to do.

My own popularity was hanging on a totally different limb than was Amber's.

Aaron Sorkin, the executive producer of *The West Wing*, had been my top client and e-mail buddy for years. And he was becoming more and more famous every single day.

Until lately, knowing a famous TV producer, or any other famous clients, never moved me. But right now, something Sorkin had done was pulling at my soul. The thing is that he created a character of a call girl, which was based on me, for his new series. And he never even asked permission nor offered to pay. After all, I feel I should be included when my personality is taken and used for whatever reason.

Sometimes when I was reading Aaron's e-mails on my Mac, I often wished I could tell the other girls at the Kit Kat about my nights in New York with him. I never did, though, until I saw Amber's appearance on *The Jenny Jones Show*. The program was one of many on which she appeared; Amber was really making the rounds.

She made me think I should get the publicity due to me. So, I shared the ordeal with her one evening while we were between clients at the Kit Kat ranch. She listened intently and was thoroughly enthused by tales of my carryings-on with Aaron.

"You know, it isn't that he based *The West Wing* call girl on me that I mind," I said. "It's that he never gave me any acknowledgement." This was the first time I'd ever mentioned Aaron to Amber.

"*The* Aaron Sorkin?" she said.

"Well, there probably is another Aaron Sorkin, but I mean *The West Wing* Aaron Sorkin.

"I've never asked Aaron for anything before," I continued.

"All that call-girl-Rob-Lowe stuff, it's been like the best publicity for the show. Nobody would have ever watched it if it weren't for you!" Amber exclaimed. "He clearly should have given you credit."

Amber is more gorgeous than anybody I ever saw on *The West Wing*, and I really just tried to do something nice for her. After she almost died, I felt getting her on *The West Wing* would restore Amber's self-esteem.

As for me, I would just come along to see Aaron. After all, he had once been my top client in New York, and he e-mailed me hundreds of times asking that I come to visit him in L.A., even though he was married.

Aaron and I hadn't seen each other in eight years!

"I just hope he'll audition you for the show, Amber," I said. "Aaron is so popular now. And hell, he can't go anywhere without having his picture taken. And it's because of the call girl episodes. So all in the cause of friendship, I will ask him."

Here is a sample message from the famed producer-writer, and I want to say, friend. Maybe friend is a little strong, but we'll know for sure after he reads this book.

Actually, I've never told anybody this, but Aaron was my best e-mail buddy when *The West Wing* premiered. Anyway, this exact message Aaron sent to me about one month before the show's premiere will floor you:

> From: ASorkin
>
> To: Dimitra
>
> Re.: The West Wing
>
> I haven't told you this yet, but on the new series a story running through the first few episodes involves the deputy communications director (played by Rob Lowe), who sleeps with a very high-priced call girl not knowing that she's a call girl. He likes her and wants to be friends with her, but of course it's a problem for the White House. I wrote it because (I'm serious about this) I've always remembered the way you came over to my apartment. I remember looking at you and thinking: I don't understand why this isn't my girlfriend.
>
> Love, Aaron

With his words etched into my mind, I just figured Aaron would allow Amber and me to be a part of his success. Of course, Amber was excited, so she and I wrote an e-mail response together while waiting for clients at the Kit Kat ranch.

On November 3, 2000, I sent another e-mail to Aaron proposing he audition Amber for a part in *The West Wing*.

From: Dimitra

To: ASorkin

Re.: Amber

Dear Aaron,

My friend Amber was on Jenny Jones talking about being assaulted. I'll send you the video. Can you audition her for *The West Wing*, please? I'm sure it would make her feel better. As for me, I'm just coming along to see you.

Love,

Dimitra

I don't know why, but for one reason or another, Aaron didn't hire my friend. However, he did play a game of tag, in a way, with e-mails.

From: ASorkin

To: Dimitra

Re.: Amber

Tell Amber I'm sorry she was assaulted. It sounds awful. I will give anybody an audition you want. As soon as I write a role in an episode she's right for. I'll talk to you about her reading for it.

Aaron

Wow, it looked like we were on our way to television. The idea sounded like fun. Amber would get a boost to her injured self-esteem, and I would actually enjoy being on the set. Everything, it seemed, was moving forward for Amber and me.

I sent another e-mail instantly.

Aaron,

Were you serious? What should we wear when we come to meet you?

Dimitra

Dimitra,

Proper attire for meeting me is sheer black nylons, heels, and a short skirt – but she should dress however she likes.

Aaron

Amber and I continued working at the Kit Kat ranch, browsed travel websites for special deals in L.A., and waited patiently to hear from Aaron about Amber's auditioning for a part in *The West Wing*.

Our hopes and plans were considerable. We would leave the ranch for a much-needed break soon and forget about the legions of horny men and the constant competition with the other girls for a while.

We would stay in Burbank, where Aaron's office was located, close enough to get there upon short notice.

Two weeks after his agreeing to audition Amber, Aaron's daughter was born. Feeling that was not the right time to contact him about Amber's part in *The West Wing*, I held off mentioning the matter. But darn, I didn't hear anything about what we had discussed in months, so by February of the New Year, 2001,

I thought I should follow up. I didn't want him forgetting his promise.

He always wrote in his e-mails that he wasn't embarrassed or ashamed of people knowing how we met, and I had believed him.

I decided to lessen my original request in hopes that something would develop quicker. So, on February 10, I sent this e-mail:

Hi Aaron,

It's probably easier if Amber and I both are just extras on *The West Wing*. Could you do that for me?

Dimitra

Without hesitation, he wrote back. And right then, I figured he was beating around the bush, so to speak.

He said:

Dimitra,

Why would you want to be an extra? It sucks. You spend all day waiting around so you can walk down the same corridor with a folder under your arm all night. You really want to do that?

Aaron

Of course I wanted it. My fingers rushed over the keyboard.

Aaron,

Yes, we both want to do it. Thank you.

I waited anxiously in front of my laptop until the computer screen changed and a new mail notification popped on.

It was from Aaron.

Dimitra,

Well, okay then. They're in a union, but I'm allowed to use a couple of non-union extras in each show. I'll let you know when.

Aaron

Again, time passed without any extra parts becoming available for Amber or me. But soon, Aaron would get other issues – those involving the pesky police at the Burbank Airport in Los Angeles.

That happening just seemed to pop out of the blue after we talked about me and Amber being extras on *The West Wing*. Aaron was arrested for trying to carry weed, magic mushrooms, and crack cocaine onto a plane in April.

A few days after the news was out, I sent him another e-mail, as a joke, you know.

On April 22, I wrote:

Dear Aaron,

If you're feeling stressed out, sometimes it helps to think of happy scenes, maybe a pastoral field, a babbling brook. You're there on a lovely summer's day, holding someone's head under the water. Now you're letting them up for a second, then, blam! Back into the freezing water, over and over again! There! Feel better?

Dimitra

The e-mail must really have cheered Aaron up a bit, because he wrote me back the same day:

Dimitra,

You're hilarious! When I'm through with whatever the law has in store for me, I want to spend the night in Las Vegas getting unbelievably high. Will you come?

Aaron

This surely hurt because for months, I had been asking him for a tiny favor that would have made a world of difference for Amber and me, and he had ignored us.

Now he was asking me to go to Las Vegas with him and get high?

I finally realized that Aaron had never been my friend. He'd never done anything for me besides pay me for sex.

Soon Aaron's problems with the law got resolved, and he claimed he was too busy with work to see Amber and me. This, I imagined, was just an excuse not to let us come. I really don't understand why, though.

It seemed pretty obvious to me, though, that Aaron was basking in the publicity triumph over his drug arrest; Amber and I were not at all on his mind.

The media put emphasis on Aaron's visit to rehab a few years prior, but Martin Sheen and others from *The West Wing* cast were publicly saying how shocked they were that he was using drugs.

"Are you going to tell Aaron he's in the book?" Amber was asking anxiously now, sitting in my kitchen, pouring Bailey's into her coffee mug.

"How can I not?" I said. "I'm going to put his e-mails in there. Everything is just great. I'm happy about the book, but I'm not 'happy happy.'"

Though we were discussing Aaron Sorkin and my book, my mind kept flashing to the recently acquired heartthrob of my dreams.

"You should see Vincent," I said. "Oh Amber, he is so hot. He actually thinks I write for magazines. And he hasn't even tried to pick me up, which is really confusing," I said.

"Why on earth would you want to get involved with your landlord?"

"I don't. I just want to have sex with him. And I want him to want to have sex with me." My face was heating up. Amber just didn't understand.

"You can't sleep with your landlord. That would be unethical," she said, almost preaching.

"Really?"

What about sleeping with the only man, historically, who didn't come on to me? I thought.

Before she left that day, Amber made me promise to think about starting a blog.

"You've got to have one," she stressed. "You can get so much publicity just from talking about the kinky things you did with your famous Mister West Wing."

Amber said good-bye and left for downtown, and I was left at my apartment with my soon-to-happen encounter with Jake.

My eyes fell to the new black La Perla bra and thong I had laid out on my white canopy-draped bed.

Sometimes being a call girl can be as stressful as boot camp. Like today, when my heart was not in my job.

Sometimes I think that I could be doing something less stressful. I could be living the non-call girl life and relaxing in someplace like Germany. So I wouldn't have any Hollywood producers to write about, but there are other benefits, none of which came to mind right away, but I was sure I would think of something positive.

Within the hour, Jake and I would have sex. I had to get ready for him. I looked at the sexy garments I was about to put on, the lacy black La Perla bra and thong. *What a total waste of lingerie,* I thought.

I was sure Vincent would like me in the La Perla set.

Chapter Two

I applied Lush Flying Fox shower gel over my body and then set the shower nozzle to the gentle massage mode. The hot flow rolled over my back until I was totally relaxed and my mind lost itself in the perfumed froth now bubbling over my bright red toenails. Wrapping myself in a large bath towel, I slipped into my new black, four-inch Jimmy Choo stilettos and walked toward the full-length mirror in the bedroom.

The clicking of designer stiletto heels on my apartment's hardwood floors always reminds me that there are good reasons why I live the call-girl life in Reno, rather than a so-called ordinary respectable life in a German suburb. In general, I am satisfied with the life-altering career decision I made at an early age. I couldn't be happier if I were the CEO of a big advertising agency signing multi-million dollar deals with IBM and American Express.

Without further ado, let me present to you the map that led to where I am today:

Stiletto heels and photography. Confused? I'll explain.

First, envision my Jimmy Choos with heels at least four inches. They were not invented for such mundane chores as walking through shopping malls, department stores, supermarkets, and parking lots – or for such projects as cleaning, laundry, or cooking.

I don't enjoy going shopping because that would require that I walk through summer-hot and icy-cold parking lots to get to stores. In other words, Jimmy Choo spikes are made for undertakings that are slightly more shameless. So, rather than go out to shop, I buy everything I wear on the Internet and eat in restaurants or call for take-out.

My mother, who wore three-inch heels, at the most, was obsessed with the hardwood flooring throughout our house in

Germany. She was heavily into dressing my brother and me in running shoes so we wouldn't scratch the floor.

Mom's ambition was to send me to college to earn an engineering degree. (That was the desirable profession in our family.)

She could never understand why I hated the mere thought of engineering so much. But you see, for me to become an engineer would mean I'd have to wear spiritless pants and nerdy glasses like the rest of my family. Male and female, they all dressed exactly like Bill Gates.

Though I'm sure lots of twelve-year-olds would simply jump at the chance to be engineers, the highly scientific profession just wasn't for me. My talents led in more creative directions.

By the time of my first memory, I spent most of my days alone in my room sketching, drawing, and painting with watercolors and oils. I painted anything that came into my head, be it ideas, images, whatever. I painted Cerberuses, centaurs, and mermaids. Birds in flight, and flowers opening. Butterflies across sapphire blue skies.

I would be a painter.

Other children used to make fun of me because I was not gleeful like them. They all teased me and called me "Foreigner" because my parents were from Greece. And yet I had blue eyes and blonde hair.

I was beautiful; I realized that. I had only my beauty to protect me.

Fashion was also necessary to me as a means of self-expression, because it enabled me to say something important about who I was, or who I wanted to be. Every time my little girlfriends came to visit, we pretended to be fashion models and played dress-up. Can you imagine me, a tiny blonde girl stumbling over my mother's precious shining floors in her size eight three-inch heels?

"Girls! You're messing up the floor," she scolded. "You look like those sluts on MTV." She was referring to Donna Summer and Olivia Newton John, both top-of-the-charts at the time. "They're singers, not sluts," I tried to explain. "They get paid a lot of money to make music videos."

"So. What's that got to do with you? You are going to college to be an engineer," she said.

"Mom…" But she never gave me a chance to say more.

"Stop wearing my shoes. Wash off that makeup! Don't you girls have homework?"

What Mom didn't know, nor did anyone else for that matter, was that I wanted to be *more* sluttish if that meant I could be in a music video on MTV.

"Why do you always say that dresses make me look sluttish?" I asked.

"Because you're a tomboy, Dimitra," she replied.

"I'm not a tomboy. Why do you say that?"

"Because, you look so cute in those corduroy pants and T-shirts I bought you last week."

My mom obviously didn't want me to grow into a woman. I came into this world when she was only seventeen, and I think she always felt she had to compete with me about who was the prettiest or the thinnest. It seemed my growing up was a bigger struggle for her than it was for me. I think I made her feel old. MTV made her feel old.

Speaking of MTV, there was one pair of pants in my closet that I really did believe looked cool on me. And I would have worn them every day if Mom had allowed it.

I loved my old faded Levi jeans, which were a little ripped around the back so my ass fell out a bit, just like those worn by those sexy girls on MTV. I remember Mom telling me that if I didn't throw those pants away, I was going to become a drug addict. But I never believed her when it came to that. Every one of my friends at school wore ripped jeans, and they never showed up with any drugs.

Mom's plans and my own just didn't mesh. And New York City certainly wasn't part of Mom's plan for me, but it was part of mine. Most of the time, I fantasized about moving to New York and wearing provocative clothes and high-heeled shoes and being in illustrious videos like Madonna made.

Still, Mom's insistence that I become an engineer came up in almost every childhood conversation I can remember. Let me tell you about a time Mom started in on me at the dinner table when I was about twelve years old.

"Dimitra, have you decided yet what kind of engineer you want to be? We need to plan your college."

"Mom, you know I want to be a painter. I don't need college for that."

"Painting isn't a serious career. It is a hobby. You can do anything you like in your spare time. After you become an engineer."

"Mom, listen," I pleaded. "My teachers say we should enjoy the careers we choose."

"Well, I know when you start college you'll like engineering. Right now, you can't know whether you'll like anything if all you do is watch music videos."

"Mom – "

"No more discussion," she retorted.

My dad, an engineer, was constantly away on business trips. We never got along much, anyhow, and mostly tried to avoid each other. My brother, Stefan, is three years younger than me; he became an engineer. No one in my family showed any real interest in what I wanted. My family was also completely unknowing about two significant facts:

First, underneath the long pants everyone was used to seeing me in wasn't a tomboy at all, but an extremely feminine body.

Second, I already knew I could support my dream of going to New York to become an artist, even if my parents wouldn't.

I was up at night reading *The Happy Hooker*, a very popular book in the Stuttgart library. All twelve-year-olds, including me, had read it at least once. Although I was shocked beyond belief by the author's outrageous exploits, and though I was still a virgin, I refused to believe that what Xaviera did was bad.

I thought of all the shameless things she did for cash. But at least she could pick and choose with whom she did them. Wouldn't it be worse to do these things with a man who is mean to you? I knew my parents were unhappily married. But my mother always pretended that everything between my dad and her was great. I realized that wasn't so, though. She tried to make it work by being very accommodating and passive with my dad.

I often thought she would be better off if she were divorced, like almost all my friends' parents. Mom didn't want a divorce, though, but I don't know why. Unfortunately however, no matter how hard our parents tried to keep up appearances, my brother and I always knew about their arguments.

School was a great diversion for me. There, I didn't think about engineering, and I didn't think about my parents' feuding. I was free-spirited.

One of my art teachers gave me an issue of *Photo* magazine once. In it were some cold, yet stylish, portraits of nude models by the German photographer Helmut Newton, and I became instantly intrigued. His controversial layouts were equivalent to *The Happy Hooker*.

I abandoned painting and became infatuated with photography. Mom and Dad thought that my photography was nothing more

26

than teenage rebellion, just as they considered the rock music I listened to and the ripped jeans I wore. I always hoped they would see me for who I was, but I guess they had too many problems with each other to take the time to know me. Honestly, (please don't tell anyone because you know how worked up some religious groups get), at age twelve I was already as skeptical about the institution of marriage as most feminists are today – although I didn't know about them yet.

After I finished high school, I couldn't move out of my parent's house fast enough. I moved to Dusseldorf, 450 kilometers north of Stuttgart, near the Belgian-German border. There, I got a job working in a quaint restaurant in the oldest part of town and lived in an apartment upstairs.

The week I turned nineteen, I lost my virginity to a young film student whom I had met in the restaurant one evening. He was two years older than me, blonde, and smoked Camel cigarettes. I remember the brand so well because of the non-filter. He could sometimes bring me to orgasm through oral sex, but never through intercourse. Never.

I could not understand the obsession people had with sex. I wasn't interested in sex. I really wasn't. I was interested in the nightlife of Dusseldorf. Like in most large, bustling cities, business was done by day; but when night fell, the city truly came to life. The city was exciting. I would lean on my windowsill watching lights twinkling around the town.

I could see men and women walking through the streets and alleys. Their footsteps, their shouting and laughter echoed round. The crowds drifted in and out. Music wafted from shops, restaurants, and bars that kept their doors open day and night.

Honestly, I had been waiting to live on my own forever, it seemed. Now, I couldn't get enough of all the bars and clubs in the city's trendy Old Town. And clubs were many and of all types.

I had just finished my shift at the restaurant one night when Teresa, another waitress at the restaurant, asked me to go with her to Valentino's. Wow! I had heard about the provocative club enough since I had come to the city. It was well known as being run by and for lesbians.

I was completely speechless. Teresa always dressed in short skirts and lacy tops. She was a beauty, with shimmering dark hair flowing down her back and dazzling green eyes that looked like two shiny emeralds. Lesbians were supposed to wear black leather vests covered with studs and shave their heads and have tattoos etched into every inch of their skin, so I'd heard.

It's a perfect cover, I thought. No one would suspect that a sexy girl like Teresa would try to get into the pants of someone so innocent as me. She saw my shocked expression and laughed out loud. "Well, now you know that I like girls," she said. "Sorry if I upset you, but I'm not hitting on you. I'm just inviting you because you seem cool. You're artistic and you're new in town." Teresa drew me in. She was living proof of the diversity of the world.

Valentino's was designed to look exactly like a cave, with huge rocks to sit on throughout.

And hearing each other talk was nearly impossible; rock music from the all-girl band slammed all through the smoky dens. Giant speakers in every corner made the faux-rock walls shake with each thump of the bass.

Girls danced with other girls, grinding together, talking, and kissing. I opened my eyes wide. Glancing around, I was amazed to see the many types of women from city-business to punk-rock chicks.

I'd never seen such female variety in a club.

I was intimidated by the women who stopped to turn and look at me. I really had to make an effort to avoid eye contact with anyone, but it happened anyway. While Teresa inched her way to the bar to order drinks, I sat on a rock-like chair near the dance floor. A woman walked by. She looked straight at me, and, to my horror, our eyes locked. Realizing what had happened, I looked away. It was too late, though. Without looking back, I knew the woman was watching me. I knew it would take very little encouragement to have her come over.

"I saw that little scene a while ago," uttered Teresa, when she returned with our drinks. She obviously could see my embarrassment.

"I guess she thinks you're looking," she teased. I just sat there, dumbly staring at Teresa.

"Don't worry about it," she added, still giggling.

"I tried not to look at her, I swear," I said.

Teresa did not believe me when I said that I had never thought of having sex with a woman. Her attitude was that you couldn't know if you liked something until you tried it.

The reason I told Teresa about my plan to go to New York and become a call girl was because she was one of those people who are into everything: sex, art, body piercing (before piercing was popular).

You know the type.

She found men gross and unappealing, she said. "But honey, I wouldn't mind having sex with them and taking their money. Hey, you know what, I think I'll go with you to New York," she announced.

Surprisingly, I later discovered that a lot of call girls are lesbians. Personally, I never thought of sex in those days, with either men or women. There was too much else going on, and it was exciting enough being a nineteen-year-old living on my own.

As time passed, I knew that I had to put my mind into actually getting to New York. I was obsessed with the city. I was ready to hop on a plane headed for JFK. Having Teresa along would make the move especially good. She had no fear.

Sometimes I used to wonder what my mother would think if she knew that my new best friend was a lesbian. And what would she think if she knew Teresa and I had been smoking weed together at least once a week since I had come to Dusseldorf, and oh God, our becoming regulars at Valentino's? I fondly thought of the ripped jeans I'd worn as a pre-teen and how Mom had warned me that they would turn me into a drug addict.

I want to tell you about my "almost" career in photography. Because photography is the second reason I became a call girl. That's because the chance of becoming a successful photographer is about the same as being abducted by an alien that looks like E.T. So I've learned.

I was so mesmerized by Helmut Newton's work that I would have had sex with anybody to have as much talent. Unfortunately, talent is not something that you can get by sleeping with someone.

I frequently visited Newton's exhibit in the Art Museum of Dusseldorf. In fact, I visited the facility so often that my name got on the mailing list. When Andy Warhol was scheduled to appear at the museum, I received a personal invitation in the mail.

Actually meeting the artist was beyond thrilling for me. I politely asked him to sign the red patent-leather purse Teresa had given me for my birthday.

Although Warhol didn't speak a lot during the entire time he was at the museum, I didn't think that he was anti-social. He seemed to pay attention to what others were saying. And when I spoke with him and told him that I wanted to move to New York, he wrote the address and phone number of his personal studio on a note and handed it to me. I was so moved by this unaccustomed glamour that I instantly began planning my career as a photographer.

About that time, Teresa's girlfriend, Hannah, an advertising executive, introduced me to Thomas. He took photographs of very expensive furniture for slick magazines. You know, his studio was the size of Dusseldorf International Airport, at least.

I was thrilled to be one of his many assistants, and the only female.

Ironically, the assistants with the most experience, like Robert, always had to carry such heavy things as cameras and backdrops. They also had to paint walls and clean floors, and the most inexperienced one – that being me – mostly had to sit on butter-soft Italian leather couches and chat with the photographer's wife, who was also his model. Thomas didn't want her to get bored between shoots.

Maybe that was the reason his other assistants never spoke to me. You might not believe this, but it was a stressful job. I could feel animosity from all the male assistants. They loathed me, and I couldn't figure out why. I did as Thomas asked of me and as often as possible, I watched him work. After all, he was probably the most important person there, and I tried to ask him important photography questions.

The more I got to chitchat with him about Hasselblad versus Nikon cameras and lenses and filters, the meaner the other assistants became. It seemed to me they wanted to talk to the boss, but were afraid to. At the same time, it seemed they should just say something to him if that was what they wanted to do. I had to do something. I had to say something. So I did.

"Good morning," I said cheerfully, when Robert walked into the ultrachic break-room on the top floor where I was drinking coffee. He frowned, but said nothing.

"Only a very superficial person would be afraid of Thomas," I said. Without acknowledging me, Robert sat down and started reading the newspaper.

"Just because Thomas's house is bigger than Dusseldorf and he owns seven cars, doesn't mean that you can ignore me and treat me like shit," I added. He continued reading, so I kept on talking.

"You don't even say good morning to me."

He glanced up angrily.

"What the fuck do you want?" he said, menacingly. He obviously was not into a nineteen-year-old giving him a lecture. He glared at me and said, "You're really annoying."

"I'm a person, Robert. I'm just as good as you. How come you don't treat me like one? How come no one except Thomas and his wife talks to me?" I was angry now, and I am sure it was obvious.

"Because you probably got this job by sleeping with somebody. Didn't you?" he hissed, slamming the paper down so hard that for a second I thought he had cracked the gorgeous glass table.

"Is that what you think? You are one-hundred-and-fifty-percent sick. You know what, don't ever talk to me! You're sick." My normally calm voice had broken into a yell. I stared at him for a moment, then stomped from the room and fled down the spiral staircase.

I flopped onto a big, soft yellow couch – a new piece of furniture that had just arrived. The new sofa cooled my temperature. I was beyond upset with Robert. I mean he wasn't exactly a smart person. He didn't realize that, according to Xaviera Hollander, men like Thomas would pay me so much money for sleeping with them that I probably wouldn't need a job at all.

Hadn't Robert read *The Happy Hooker*? I wasn't sure of too many things yet, but one thing was quite simple: nobody has to sleep with someone just to get a job.

I would never tell Robert this, but I only became a call girl because I'm not as brilliantly talented as Helmut Newton, or

Thomas. But I really loved photography. I loved photography so much that it wouldn't have mattered to me how I had to make a living while trying to get as good as Newton or Thomas.

I realized that it would be easier to sell my body for cash than it was to have a regular job and get accused of unethical behavior.

America would be so different, I kept telling myself. Things would be more progressive in the States. In New York, people surely wouldn't be as unenlightened as Robert. Would they? Maybe I should quit my job and become a call girl immediately, I thought. Just to spite Robert and the other assistants. But no! I wanted to wait until I got to New York. I believed that German men still lived in caves and certainly didn't deserve me anyway.

So, as well as high-heel shoes, photography definitely influenced my choice to become a call girl.

Chapter Three

With Jake on his way to my apartment, it was time for me to get dressed for our appointment.

You know, males can be very simple; they read our signals as green lights or red lights, I swear. To them, women in well-chosen, drop-dead intimate attire are a turn-on. Jake adores real boudoir babes in Marabu slippers and camisoles in pastel colors, as well as 1950s-style push-up bras and frilled panties a la Brigitte Bardot, or even risqué sheer silk gowns with lacy insets.

Actually, all my clients do. And with good reason! I mean, I always dress for them as if I were on a date with the man of my dreams.

I stood in front of the mirror and slowly bent down to bring the sheer black-mesh thong with the scalloped lace trim up over my hips. Then I adjusted the sheer matching bra with its low plunging center over my breasts. It barely covered my nipples. You can surely imagine, this was almost like having on no bra at all, but more provocative.

I honestly believe that when you are a call girl, you absolutely should wear the most extravagant lingerie. This, in my opinion, boosts your confidence and makes you look and feel alluring. Without this confidence, there would be no point in being a call girl anyway. But with confidence, if I don't like the client I'm with, and sometimes I positively don't, at least I still like myself.

After dressing and applying gloss (I almost never wear makeup, only pale lip-gloss), I sprayed my neck and damp hair with Ormonde Jayne Frangipani, which is my favorite scent, and looked at my watch. It was already 7 p.m. – exactly. Where was Jake?

Jake gets all bent out of shape whenever there is a two-cent hike in gas-prices. On the other hand, it doesn't seem to concern him at all when he drives the fifty miles from South Lake Tahoe to visit me (I'm his $400-an-hour-call-girl habit).

Also, regardless of how he feels about the high price of gas, he has this crazy idea that, in order to feel like a real man, he needs to drive something that gets only eight miles per gallon on the highway. A Lincoln Navigator. A few days ago, Jake said, "It's a shock to fill your car up for $85, but if that's what it takes to do what you have to do."

Then I said, "No, you're being pimped by greasy money-men who will sell anything to anybody and call themselves patriots."

"This is post nine-eleven," he replied. "Encouraging fuel efficiency makes you a suspect."

"Capitalism no longer goes hand in hand with democracy, Jake," I said. "Personally, for every civil liberty I lose, I go out and consume more useless goods. The fourth amendment gone, I'll go out and buy a new Ford. The first amendment, and I might even be tempted to invest in some real estate."

He laughed and he called me a revolutionary. Well, that's Jake.

He called from his cell phone soon after I'd gotten into my sexy undergarments. He was at the Victorian and had already parked the Navigator in the lot behind the building. I stayed on the phone, instructing him to type a combination of numbers in the keypad to unlock the door leading into the building and directing him to my apartment door.

I opened the door immediately.

"Hi, beautiful," he said. "It smells great in here." He paused, and sniffed. "Are you smoking weed?"

"Apparently everyone in this building smokes except me," I replied, and kissed him on the cheek. Then I took his hand and led him through the living room and into the bedroom.

Jake is a tall, blonde, athletic man who owns a window glass business in Tahoe. At forty-two years old and never been married, he "is still waiting to meet the right woman," he says. The thing

I know, which he doesn't, is that when he meets that woman, he won't know what to say or do. He's just too shy around women. This is a man who needs to be seduced. I should know.

"Make yourself comfortable. I'll fix us some orange juice," I said, smiling up at him.

When I returned with the juice, he was sitting on the edge of the bed. He had placed a white envelope on my dresser. I knew what it contained. I seldom have to ask my regular clients, like Jake, for the money, and I really never have to count it. I completely trust them. All my new clients get screened extensively before I agree to meet them. After I know them for a while, they start to feel like cozy old friends. I know this is going to sound totally spoiled, but my regular clients are utterly decent and reliable men.

"Jake, do you like my tiny, very expensive, outfit?" I teased.

"You know that I do."

Already, he was virtually hypnotized and unable to look away.

Walking to the bed, I slowly started to undress him. First, I removed his jacket and shirt. Then I unbuckled his belt and popped open his pants button. They fell to the floor, revealing boxer shorts with a colorful pattern of martini glasses. His erection was pushing against the martini glasses. He truly blushed as I pulled them off.

I took a condom from my dresser and expertly rolled it down on my client's hard dick. I smiled my most seductive smile at him; all the while, my hands caressed his blonde hair and the tanned skin on his neck and back.

"Lie down," I whispered. With Jake under me, I slowly peeled off my thong. I positioned my body over his. He cupped and squeezed my breasts through the thin, delicate material of my bra.

"Take it off," I whispered in his ear. His fingers flew to my back, and then he found the clasp of my bra and quickly opened it. Breasts free, he brushed his thumbs over my nipples while I guided him slowly into me.

He moaned out loud.

Do you think you might like a profession like mine?

Well, if you are considering working as a call girl, there are a few things you should know. Especially when it comes to obtaining clientele.

The only place to advertise is on the Internet. The Information-Super-Highway has become the main venue for a potential client to find a match. There, one is able to browse hundreds of pictures and ads of women in his area. In cyberspace, every call girl is a "provider," and the clients are "hobbyists." The Internet makes meeting a call girl as easy as ordering a double cheese pizza. Generally, the women's phone numbers and rates are provided in the ads.

It wasn't this easy pre-Internet, in the '90s, when there were only a handful of reputable escort agencies in New York City. I can't believe time has passed so quickly.

Teresa and I, at last, traveled to New York in 1990. She had broken up with her girlfriend and told everyone she was going to study computer animation and work in film or television.

All of my friends and family thought I was going to New York on vacation. And with good reason. That was what I had told everyone.

Anticipation certainly had me in its grip, squeezing and twisting my insides until they formed a knot in my throat as the Pan Am 747 crossed the Atlantic. And even more so when it dipped its wing toward the breathtaking city on its approach to John F. Kennedy International Airport. I never imagined that Manhattan would be so beautiful. I remember being overwhelmed, happily overwhelmed.

So much there reminded me of things I had seen in the movies. Glitzy skyscrapers surrounded our hotel on East 52nd. On the streets, cabs seemed to fly by. Car and truck horns, along with train whistles, blew constantly. The noises were so thrilling.

In the first twenty-four hours of arriving in the city, we strolled along the sidewalks, weaving against the flow of people. We browsed the exclusive boutiques on Fifth Avenue. And, you know, the rush of New Yorkers pressing past only facilitated our excitement to its highest possible peak. I remember feeling a surge from the lack of safety.

On our second day in The Big Apple, we looked up "Escort Services" in the Yellow Pages.

The biggest ad was that of International Escorts on West 57th Street. In fact, the ad spread across two pages in the phonebook. Teresa bravely called the number to schedule an interview for us. She talked to a very nice Swiss woman named Marie. She was one of several "bookers" at the agency, we discovered later. Bookers were very pretty, stylish, multi-national women who sat behind modern desks in a large apartment of an upscale high-rise building. Their duties mainly consisted of answering phones and arranging meetings between clients and call girls.

On our first visit to the agency, I found the place looked as I had imagined a modeling agency would look. There were loose photographs and chic portfolios of women on the coffee and end tables. We sat on a red leather sofa, nervously looking at the stunning women in the pictures. They all looked like supermodels, posing in Chanel suits and wearing expensive, gorgeous jewelry.

A pretty blonde girl brought coffee on a silver tray. She also handed us job applications and told us to read and sign.

Marie saw our nervousness and came over to join us. With my first time as a call girl imminent, I was as hyperactive as a six-year-old at Disney World. I couldn't stop tugging at the hem of my plain yellow linen sundress. I felt completely underdressed.

"There are certain hotels in Manhattan where you literally can't walk in the door unless you are dressed in a business suit," Marie said. "The Inter Continental is one of them. I just sent two of our girls there today, and they came back with $2,000 each. After you make some money, I'll go to Bloomingdale's with the two of you and help you find the perfect suits," she continued, rather presumptuously.

Manhattan really must be crawling with call girls, I suddenly thought. Women wearing business suits were everywhere you looked.

"First thing you need to do, though, is get professional pictures for our portfolio as soon as possible," she advised Teresa and me. Just as we signed our names on the bottom of our contracts, Marie's cordless phone rang. She answered it.

"Hello, International Escorts. How may I help you?" She paused. "No problem, sir. First of all, I need your name, address, listed telephone number, and driver license number."

The situation left Teresa and me momentarily stunned because it was so business-like, not at all sleazy, as we had imagined. It was as if Marie was discussing the sale of a shoe-cutting knife from an infomercial and not of a high-priced call girl who was getting paid to have sex.

"Okay, Mr. Levine," Marie continued. "Our agency provides the escort for your companionship only. What she chooses to do during that time is by her own accord and is in no way pertinent to the money you pay her."

I heard my brain click; I suddenly realized Marie had to say that for legal reasons. If she didn't, she would be simply hiring out prostitutes, and that certainly was against the law in New York City.

"So, Mr. Levine, what kind of girl are you interested in? White? Black? Asian?" she asked patiently. "What about hair color?"

Mr. Levine was in the middle of ordering a girl as if she were a pizza. But this wasn't a Hawaiian with extra pineapple; this was a real life girl with feelings, and she had people who cared about her. And what about us, I thought? We were applying to be take-out food and men would order us and have sex with us just to get their kicks.

"It's going to be three hundred per hour, sir," Marie said. "But trust me, our girls are well worth the expense. We are considered the top escort agency in Manhattan." She paused again, this time for several minutes. "I am so happy to be of service, Tom. I'll send her out as soon as I can. I hope you enjoy yourself this afternoon."

She hung up and turned to us.

"You two are real sweethearts," she said. "And don't worry. I'll make sure to only send you to nice guys, like our Tom Levine," she said, her eyes glancing at the telephone. "No druggies and no kinky stuff for you two girls. Now, have you decided what names you are going to use for International Escorts?"

This is how I became "Lisa" and Teresa became "Yasmin."

I confess that I am certain that I can't explain how I, as well as Teresa, ended up with a high-powered client in the movie business. Before the end of my first month as a call girl, a Hollywood screenwriter ordered me like takeout.

It sometimes seems like yesterday.

Teresa and I both got sent on our first assignments on the very first day working for the agency. Marie had told us to go to the Waldorf Astoria Hotel on 49th Street, where two investment bankers, Paul and Louis, were waiting for us in one of the suites.

On paper, at least, this first assignment should have been easy. All Teresa and I knew about the men were their names and the number of their suite. But, we felt sure there was a big chance they would see us naked, and we them, shortly. How hard could it be?

The famous Art Deco hotel was dazzling in its proportions, scale, and richness of materials and finish. The cavernous Park Avenue lobby was up a broad flight of stairs, and we walked past the front desk and concierge stations, lounges, bars, and luxury retail stores to locate the elevators. Dress wise, there was definitely a party theme going on in the lobby. Women in opulent gowns were weighed down with estate gems and were accompanied by men in immaculate tuxedos. Everyone was kissing everyone and walking towards one of the many hotel ballrooms used for prestigious benefits and dinners.

Without too much trouble, I located the elevators and pressed the button to the thirty-third floor. I got off the elevator bravely. Teresa followed me. I saw the suite was right next to the elevators. Teresa looked at me, took a deep breath, and knocked on the door. This was serious. There was no going back now.

Luckily, Paul and Louis were both in their late twenties, sophisticated, and attractive. But things seemed to move too swiftly. I barely had a chance to sit before Louis' hands were all over me.

"Wait a minute," I said. "I think we should call the agency first." I jumped up from the couch and grabbed the phone, which was on one of the side-tables.

The dark-haired, blue-eyed Louis said, "Forgive me, but you are very sexy. You are like a flawless commodity."

I had never heard a man compare me to a stock before, but I guess I was flattered. Still, I was determined to follow the procedure.

"You are charming," I said, as I dialed International. We had been told to call Marie as soon as we had arrived and collected our fee of $300 for the hour.

Louis was suddenly afraid that we would leave. I know, because he hurriedly pulled a thick wad of one hundred dollar bills from his jacket.

"Do you want to stay a few hours? How long can you stay?" he asked, while I waited for Marie to answer the phone. Paul and Teresa chatted on one of the sofas while Louis was ogling me from head to toe. He could not tear his eyes off me, or take a single step away from my side.

With the negotiating over, Louis paid Teresa and me $1,000 each for four hours. Soon afterwards, the men decided that Teresa and Paul would use the master bedroom; Louis and I were to stay in the smaller one. To say he was anxious to get started would be an understatement.

Louis didn't want to talk to me at all, it seemed. It was quite obvious to me that he only wanted to have sex.

He got on top of me on the king-size bed. At the time, I thought that the most peculiar thing about the situation was that Louis was really handsome. I had always thought that men who pay call girls were either ugly or old.

Back at the agency four hours later, Marie patted Teresa and me on the back when we dropped off the agency's commission. She smiled and said, "Very well done, girls."

"That was so exhausting, Marie," I said. "They were nice, but I was happy when it was over."

Marie said young guys can be tedious sometimes, and she promised the next time she would send me to someone older who would appreciate talking to a young lady like me and perhaps even pay me to go out to dinner with him.

I was still tired the next morning. While Teresa went to check out some art galleries in Soho, I spent the day in bed watching MTV.

Almost all the men I met over the following weeks were pretty much very alike. Very rich and very horny.

I managed to maintain a level of self-respect with my high-class clients because I began postponing the sex until the last possible moment. Sometimes I felt like a tease, but I was determined not to let anyone jump me as soon as I walked in the door.

I started asking new clients to order me cappuccinos or champagne from room service. Or I gave them a long massage to relax, which also killed time.

Do you want to know what I wanted more than anything in New York? More than the money, more than the designer clothes, and more than the famous restaurants?

I wanted to meet a man who was not being ruled by his penis, a man who could engage my mind. As it was, men just expected me to strip down for them upon my arrival.

Three weeks after my first client, I met that man.

At 1 a.m., I was lying in bed watching television when Marie called. She actually begged me to go to an apartment near Central Park South. She said the man she wanted me to be with was beyond sweet on the phone, and his identification and credit card checked out. I, in no way, felt like working at this wee morning hour, but Marie said the client had insisted on a redhead. So, I told her to give me the details.

"His name is Aaron Sorkin," she said, adding that his address was 120 West 60th Street, penthouse 52 B. 212 – 246 3417.

I called Aaron and told him I would be over at his place in no more than 45 minutes.

"Hmmm – do you have black stockings?" he asked, sounding a bit shy.

"Yes."

"Could you please wear them for me?"

"Okay," I replied. I hung up the phone and took a shower. As if it were only moments ago, I remember getting ready for him that night.

You should have seen the dress I had on; it was a black Versace mini-dress that was so miniscule it barely covered the tops of my stockings and garter belt. It's such a tease, that little bit of flesh that can be glimpsed when you turn a certain way, or sit down. I looked sexy but still fashionable.

Surely this guy Aaron would be all over the dress, I thought.

I arrived at his building and the uniformed doorman called Aaron's apartment to let him know that he had a visitor. I got into the mirrored elevator and exited on the top floor. I found apartment 52 B and rang the bell. The door opened.

"Aaron? Nice to meet you," I said when he opened the door.

"Are you Lisa?" he asked, seeming pleased.

I smiled in response.

"It's nice to meet you," he said, leading me from the foyer to his living room.

Everything in the penthouse, from the cherry wood and black leather furnishing to the mirrored walls and floor-to-ceiling windows over the city, was breathtaking.

"I love your view," I said, smiling cautiously. I didn't want to show too much excitement.

There is nothing more beautiful than the view of Manhattan when you see it from the window of a penthouse on the 52nd floor. The windows wrapped around the south, east, and west of the apartment.

Completely to my surprise, Aaron asked me to sit down and enjoy the view while he opened a bottle of champagne. And I hadn't even asked him for any champagne. The more I looked around his living room, the more intimidated I became. God, what if he didn't like me, I thought anxiously, as he returned with the champagne glasses. I was frightened at the possibility, although I truly appreciated that he hadn't immediately started clawing me.

"Would you like to go to the bedroom?" I asked shyly, "or are we, you know, doing it here?"

Aaron laughed as if I had made the funniest joke. This was strange, even for someone who calls escort services at 1 a.m., I thought.

"I want to relax and take it very slowly, actually," he said.

How original, I thought.

"You are so beautiful," he said, sitting opposite from me in a black leather upholstered chair. "I would like to ask you something," he continued. "If you stay all night, how much will that cost me?"

I was speechless. He was classically handsome and had the cutest lean, muscular body. He had on one of those sexy silk robes by Ralph Lauren, the ones all the rich guys wore.

What's more, I liked his personality. I liked the finesse with which he manipulated, offering and submitting before receiving or demanding.

"What do you say?" he repeated. He was so sweet.

"I have to call International," I told him. Being a call girl is great sometimes, I thought. This man was adorable. And, had it not been for my being a call girl, I might never have met him.

Another thing, I knew that by the end of the night I would be very upset if he didn't ask me to remove the Versace dress.

"Aaron, Marie said it's two thousand dollars for eight hours. Is that okay with you?"

He paid me in cash. I was pleased. *He is so adorable,* I kept thinking. And he was a screenwriter. I loved artistic men. He told me that his play *A Few Good Men* was a hit on Broadway, and it would soon be a movie with Jake Nicholson, Demi Moore, and Tom Cruise. I was being paid to spend the night with this gorgeous screenwriter, with all this creativity and talent. It would be fun, to say the least. And then suddenly, just right out of the blue, he whispered, "Do you want to see my study?" Then he said, his voice lower, "I want to get high. Do you mind?"

"No," I answered, following him into the study. "I've never tried anything but weed."

He sat behind his desk and pulled out a wooden box filled with joints and cocaine.

"You wouldn't believe the weed I have," he exclaimed. He held a joint up to my nose.

"It smells nice," I replied.

"Yeah," he said, his breath tight while he lit the smoke. He pulled me onto his lap and took a long hit. Weed or no weed, I was charmed by him. I happily got high with him. If a man isn't trying to undress me immediately, I will do anything for him.

It did occur to me that weed combined with champagne makes me very sleepy, so I told him. He immediately offered me a huge line of cocaine. And after that, when I wasn't the least bit tired anymore, I was sitting on his knee kissing him passionately and wondering when his hand would go up my dress. And even after that, after another joint, another line, and more kissing, he was definitely still the perfect gentleman, and we both still had on all our clothes.

"I love your legs," he would whisper from time to time, as he ran his fingers up and down my sheer stockings. I wanted to sleep with him. He was a client, and I was not supposed to want to sleep with him. But I realized he was right when he told me that really great sex is about building anticipation and that restraint can be very erotic. When he touched and kissed me over the smooth satin of my dress, I felt more naked than naked.

This was the best night of my young life.

Chapter Four

Of course, I had no idea what to do about it, but something strange happened to me the day I met Vincent. Extremely shameless thoughts of this Ed Burns look-alike persisted and were getting into the way of my writing. For the previous few weeks, I had been deep into research for a story about penguin prostitutes, an extremely interesting topic. Still, I just couldn't get Vincent off my mind.

For me, this is really saying something. Honestly, I have never been on a manhunt for a date or my soulmate, or anything tiresome like that. But like an infatuated schoolgirl, I fell for Vincent the second I laid eyes on him. Not like me. Wanting to do shameless things with a man for free is not at all me. I'm not easily stimulated in that way – perhaps because the sex I've had as a call girl hasn't been particularly satisfying.

My focus is pouring my heart into writing about the desires and frailties of both call girls and clients. So from where were all these thoughts about Vincent coming?

He was an outstanding landlord. Without tenants asking, he found things in the building to fix. He seemed to love parking his Hummer in the back where he chatted with Fred, our maintenance man.

Concentration was impossible with Ed Burns looming. I am still not sure if it was Vincent or the Ed Burns in him.

After I first moved into my apartment in the Victorian, Vincent called me on my cell phone one day and asked if I would like him to bring over a portable heater. According to Vincent, the central heat in the building was out of order and a cold front was predicted. I explained that I hadn't noticed that the heat wasn't working. And even though it was the beginning of November, it was warm enough inside my apartment. Then I wondered, quite ecstatically, if perhaps his bringing over a heater could be his strategy to try to seduce me. This might be Vincent's way to break the ice. Maybe he was secretly as attracted to me as I was to him? He'd acted aloof and distant when he showed me the apartment.

Now, if he liked me and were to ask me out, naturally I would say no. It's important not to seem too eager if you want to get into any kind of shameless position with a man who looks like Ed Burns.

I tried to relax; yet picking the right outfit to wear for Ed Burns was a huge stress; finally, I settled on my Juicy jeans and white tank top, all the while my nerves were in total shreds. I hoped that Vincent, of course, seeing the white top with the no-bra-look, wouldn't take no for an answer.

Wearing this outfit in a public place would cause unknown men to whistle, shout, and beep the horns of their vehicles.

Hopefully, Vincent would understand that I wanted his attention – and him. He would surely persist in expressing his interest in me, as do the many men who harass me, whether verbally or by staring.

As a call girl, I get paid very well for my company. So, in order for me to have free sex with Vincent, because this man was just so adorable, I would at least have to play hard to get.

On the record, my sudden actions and feelings for Vincent were his fault because he was the most irresistibly handsome man in all of Reno.

And when he came over, he appeared even cuter than I remembered him. He wore a long black coat, black jeans, and the exact sunglasses Keanu Reeves wore in *The Matrix*. The moment he walked through the doorway, the atmosphere in my apartment was highly charged. Vincent has these amazingly sculpted, full, dark lips that managed to look strong yet delicate at the same time, which fascinated me and made me really horny. I maintained my composure, though, and watched him push the strange contraption of a heater into my living room. Then we stood for a moment looking at each other.

I said, in a sweet voice, "Thank you, Vincent. When are they going to fix the central heating?"

"This week sometime," he said, still eyeing me. "Meanwhile, I hope the weather stays nice." He pointed to the portable heater. "I don't have too many of these."

I let my fingers rub over Kenny's back; my cat was sleeping on top of his favorite pillow on the sofa, right next to my laptop. And, oh no, on my computer screen was the research article about penguin prostitutes!

I hoped Vincent wouldn't notice it. Then I suddenly realized that I was worried about nothing because he was scrutinizing my white tank top. Apparently, by the expression on his face, he was mesmerized by it. In fact, he seemed almost as mesmerized as I was by him. I mean the way he looked, especially his obscenely luscious mouth.

Vincent and I just stood there silently for what seemed the longest time. The electricity was overpowering. But he made no play for me. What was wrong with the guy?

I know that straight men will say and do anything for sex. They'll lie, they'll cheat, they'll steal, and they'll put it on Visa, literally. But he didn't say a thing. He clearly was not the aggressive type. And I found myself trying to figure out how I could let him know that I'd liked him since the first time I'd walked into his office.

All of a sudden, Vincent's eyes moved to a long, blue Ralph Lauren lace dress I had hung over the bathroom door to wear for a client later that day. He stared at the dress, looked at me, then back at the dress, as if totally surprised. The dress was almost see-through, but I only planned to wear it inside the apartment.

Vincent should see me dressed and made up, I thought.

That second, I decided that someone had to say something. I whispered, "Vincent, would you like to go out with me sometime?"

What? I hadn't meant to say that at all, I thought, scolding myself. I had just asked a man out. One thing I know is that men are the ones who are supposed to ask *me* out.

A few seconds later, he answered my offer. "Sure," he said. Then in another moment, he glanced toward my laptop and Kenny.

"Pretty cat. What's her name?"

"It's a he. His name is Kenny," I replied.

"As in South Park?"

"Yes," I said, giggling. He smiled and gave me a look that I can safely describe as very shameless, if you know what I mean. Then, he walked slowly to the door. Turning back to me he said, "Okay, I'll see you later." Then he was gone. Of course, I couldn't write a thing for a whole week.

I sat on my couch and tried to think of something to compose, but every sentence I wrote involved the name Vincent.

On a particularly cold day the week after he brought the heater to me, I wandered upon Vincent in the basement laundry room where he was helping Fred fix a broken washing machine. Vincent hustled about moving one of Fred's toolboxes out of the way. His shirt was off, and I watched the sinewy muscles on his back. I could see that all the lifting and hammering he did while working on the apartment building had paid off. I eyed him all over.

And he eyed me.

We did all the things people do: making eye contact and smiling mysteriously and impishly. He stared at my chest, then at my butt. (He had a habit of staring at my chest and butt when we passed in the hallway.)

But I couldn't get my message across to him. He had never said anything more than a flirtatious "Hi," or simply my name. When was he going to ask me out? He couldn't expect me to ask him again.

It was torture…he flirted with me and then didn't do anything about it. And I couldn't just hang out in the basement and wait for him to make a move. You can imagine how beyond confused I was.

Another time he showed up at my apartment door to borrow a pen. His quick visit that day was totally unexpected. I quickly had to hide a pair of unbelievably gorgeous black stockings that had been on my coffee table (just in case Mr. Wealth came calling) before opening the apartment door.

Truthfully, to most people who don't know me very well, including Vincent, I don't appear to be a call girl at all. They think of me as the girl-next-door, and not the beguiling vixen I present to my clients.

Ken, the retired man in the apartment next to mine, once caught a glimpse of me dressed in only lingerie and high heels.

He completely freaked me out when I opened the door expecting the client I was waiting for.

I tried to keep my call girl activities to a minimum. I certainly didn't want Vincent paying any attention to any vicious rumors.

I didn't know if Ken had told anyone about the wealthy businessmen who often visited me, or that I had freely answered the door in skimpy European lingerie and Jimmy Choos.

When Vincent showed up, practically out of nowhere, and looking hot every time, it was agony. Believe me, the mere presence of him made me feel almost as crazy as I felt after the few times I smoked crack cocaine with Aaron.

I knew nothing about crack, not even cocaine, before that first night with Aaron.

It seemed that he liked getting high almost as much as he liked writing. Exactly one week after our first date (if that's what you want to call it), Aaron phoned me directly and asked me to spend the night with him. He assured me he would pay me $2,000 for the night. He had not called the agency, which meant I could keep all the money to myself. I felt a little guilty because I was cutting out Marie; however, I was flattered that he liked me. I would be a fool to say no. I felt really special because we had not experienced sex other than kissing and hugging, not yet anyway, not even a Bill-Clinton-no-sex-blowjob.

Shortly after I arrived at Aaron's penthouse, he pulled a small, strange object out of a brown paper bag. Excited, he showed me a glass pipe.

"What's that?" I asked.

"It's a pipe," he said, looking me straight in the eye. "I'd like to smoke some cocaine if it's okay with you." I had no idea what he meant, but I remember feeling very scared in the huge penthouse for the first time.

Even now, I can see the pipe in my mind. To me, it looked like something that would belong to a desperate and depressed soul in the Bronx or Harlem, and not to a young, handsome, talented screenwriter living in a Manhattan penthouse, surrounded by success. I was so shocked that I didn't know what to say in response to his unfamiliar request. I don't remember saying anything.

Then he got up and walked to the kitchen. After a few minutes, I followed him.

He put some cocaine powder in a coffee cup. Then he added baking soda, and he put the cup into the microwave. Just like a Pop-tart, I thought. Soon afterwards, he brought out a hard, white, rock-like substance that he placed in the pipe. He placed Don Henley's *End of the Innocence* in the CD player and snuggled up to me on the leather living room sofa. He was completely nude, but at his request, I was still fully clothed.

"You don't have to do it if you don't want to," he said, casually.

"Okay," I said.

Until that night, and though he had introduced me to cocaine on our first meeting, I knew nothing of crack. But he apparently liked it, so I thought it must be cool.

He held the lighter to the pipe and heated the glass surface until the rocks inside melted completely and turned into a hot, watery liquid. He closed his eyes, brought the pipe to his lips, and then inhaled slowly and deeply. With his eyes still closed, he held the smoke in his lungs for several moments, and then slowly exhaled a colorless cloud through his nostrils.

Aaron was suddenly very cheerful. The things he'd barely noticed earlier, like the black leather miniskirt and silky blouse I had worn for him, now enthralled him completely.

He became extremely affectionate, stroking my hair over and over and telling me how good it smelled. He said he liked everything about me, especially my legs. He honestly convinced me that I had the best-looking legs he had seen in his entire life.

Despite my concerns and fears, when he asked me if I wanted to try the crack, I said yes.

I wasn't really too excited about such an experience, but I was secretly afraid that if I didn't accept his offer he would think of me as totally square. I told myself I was only doing as any good call girl would. Thus being to please and play along.

So he held the pipe to my lips and I inhaled very slowly, as he had instructed. I held my breath, exactly as he had.

Smoking crack was like no sensation I had ever felt. Even if I wouldn't describe it as a good feeling, it was certainly an exciting one, almost like being on a roller coaster.

One minute I was flying, the next I was falling, and the next I was being rocked sideways.

Aaron was so attentive now. He brought me shots of cognac and champagne in beautiful crystal glassware. And we made out on the sofa like two teenagers. He wrapped his ankles around mine while we kissed to the music of Don Henley.

He removed my skirt and blouse snaillike.

To this day, he is the only man who ever asked me to leave on my shoes, my stockings, garter belt, and bra during our trysts.

We laughed and kissed and giggled all night at silly things, even at how awesome the West Side Highway looked from the 52nd floor, with the way it snakes through Manhattan.

Then something amazing happened. We had intercourse on the sofa with all the lights on, right in front of the floor-to-ceiling window, with all of Manhattan being able to watch us. While he lay on his back, I straddled his lap and lowered myself onto his penis. I liked that position because it gave him an eyeful, and I had more freedom to place myself in the most stimulating position; plus, we were face-to-face, which allowed for lots of kissing.

I don't think he could get enough of me, and I know I couldn't get enough of him.

The only thing that slightly freaked me out, other than that initial introduction to crack cocaine, was this: Aaron had told me he was single, you know, unattached. But in reality, he had a fiancé.

I found this out by accident. He had given me his telephone number and insisted that I call him whenever I felt like talking. So, you know me, I did exactly that. Once when I called, a female voice came on the line.

"Hello?"

"Hi," I said. "I would like to speak with Aaron."

"Who is this?" asked the woman on the other end.

"This is Lisa," I replied, a bit confused. But she could have been a maid. So I asked, "Who is this?"

"This is his fiancé."

"Oh. Okay. Please tell him that I called." I hung up.

You can imagine my astonishment. After all, I had been convinced he was single.

Men are so strange when they meet call girls. I couldn't imagine what difference it made to him whether I thought he was single or engaged. To a call girl, it doesn't matter at all if a man is single, engaged, or married. And certainly, a whole night with him each time I saw him was a long time, but he was still a client. When a man pays a call girl for companionship, especially when one pays as well as Aaron did, a girl doesn't need to work the rest of the week. You are very lucky to have a client like this. The worst thing you can do is screw it up by getting emotionally attached to him.

Still, I was very tempted to let my feelings develop for him, and I always felt as if he had feelings for me, too. Our nights together were totally sick in the most awesome way. Aaron was fun and sweet and one of the nicest men I had ever met. In addition to all this bliss, the money was great.

Of course, I wondered sometimes, in theory only, what it would be like to be engaged to someone like Aaron. But no sooner than the thought would come, I would dismiss it completely.

So, suddenly I found myself having been a call girl for three whole months. But with the way time had flown by, it seemed more like three minutes.

I looked back over this period…and had to laugh. I, Dimitra, from Drama, Greece, had become a high-priced Manhattan call girl. The clothes on my body told of shopping sprees on Fifth Avenue. Nothing else about me or on me proved that I was one of the highest paid escorts in New York. I felt as if I had cheated: that was why I laughed.

How could it be that my features were still so pure?

I had innocent, large blue eyes that fascinated my wealthy clients, and an adolescent mouth that they wanted to kiss.

I was obsessed with my beauty, initiated in the art of seduction, laughing at the men who were lusting after me. I played the submissive woman and charmed them. I gave myself to them in pleasure with perfect indifference. I was offered to anyone who could afford me, but was forever inaccessible…how could it be that such a life had made my body so resplendent?

I was having more fun than I could ever have imagined.

By this time, Teresa had moved to L.A. to pursue her career in computer animation; she enrolled in the prestigious Pasadena Art Center and continued in call girl side-work for the famous Madam Alex in Beverly Hills. Meanwhile, I had moved into a one-bedroom apartment on East 53rd Street in mid-town Manhattan. My new pad was cute and very expensive, but I didn't care.

Can you imagine how divine it all was? Everything was so perfect.

I rarely had to work for International anymore to pay rent or for the purchase of Versace mini-dresses or La Perla lingerie. Despite the fact that I was still officially a call girl, I really didn't work, because spending nights with Aaron didn't feel like work at all.

"I'm sorry," I said, apologizing to Marie when she called once quite unexpectedly.

She wanted to know why I hadn't been available to go on any assignments.

"I'm trying to get into photography," I said.

I felt badly that I had to lie to her. But how could I tell her that I had stolen one of her best clients from right under her nose? I knew she would be beyond mad at me. So, I decided to work every now and then just to keep up appearances with International Escorts.

This conversation with Marie inspired me to buy a new Minolta camera and start taking pictures of the incredible city in which I was living.

This I did. As well as taking photographs of New York City, my new camera opened many doors for me.

The next time I went to a concert at the Roseland Theater, the security guards let me stand near enough to the stage to get close-up shots of the hip-hop group, A Tribe Called Quest, which was just on the verge of super-stardom.

I even met one of the event promoters, a cute blonde man named James, who reminded me a lot of Brad Pitt. At the time, Brad Pitt was starting to emerge as a super-star.

James thought I was a professional photographer, not a professional call girl. He introduced himself, and pestered me to give him my phone number.

He was very persistent. He even offered me backstage passes for the Madonna concert that was coming in a few weeks.

Finally, just before I left the concert, I gave in and presented him with my number. At that time, Aaron was decidedly the main picture for me. The only trouble was that his screenplay of *A Few Good Men* was being made into a motion picture. This meant that once filming began, he would be spending a lot of time in L.A. But as far as I knew, that was still one year away.

Getting back to the research for my penguin prostitutes story:

It is noted that examples of penguin prostitution were observed in Adelie penguins on Ross Island, which is about 800 miles from the South Pole.

Two professors studied the actions of male penguins as they paid female penguins for sexual favors with rocks and stones. The professors described how the penguins all hunt for stones, which are a limited resource that is crucial for their survival. Once all the loose rocks have been collected, the penguins attempt to construct a nesting platform, key for keeping eggs high and dry above the area's mud and chilly water melts. Stones are so valuable to these penguins that they steal from each other and risk being attacked by the penguin owning the hard currency. But rather than steal, the female penguin exchanges sex for rocks.

A female will wander off from her partner to a nest of an unpaired male. She presents herself to him by flirting, and if he shows interest, she will lie face down for him to perform sex. After the mating is over, she picks up her payment, usually one stone, and carries it to her own platform.

Sometimes, the females will return for a second helping without having to offer more sex. Research shows that with a little flirting, the male will frequently allow the female to first play with a rock, and then cart it away. One clever female managed to collect 62 stones with flirtation only.

She was a tease.

Chapter Five

I had finished writing the chapter in this book about the penguin prostitutes when noises in the hallway of the Victorian glided into my dream and startled me to consciousness.

I heard someone whispering.

"If she doesn't," pause, "could be bad," pause, "might actually report us to the police."

"There is no way she doesn't smoke pot. Hell, everybody smokes." This time the muffled voice was that of a woman. Footsteps creaked closer to my door.

"Sshh! You two! She'll hear you. I'm going to talk to her."

A door closing produced an echo from somewhere down the hall. Still there was babbling. I wasn't expecting anyone this time of morning. The dull voices got closer until they stopped outside my apartment door.

Kenny leapfrogged from the bed and raced into the kitchen. When he hears noises near the door, he sneaks into one of the cabinets and hides. All became silent.

Suddenly, there were loud coughs. Apparently, these nice people were smoking weed in front of my apartment and having a conversation at 8 a.m. My lucky day, I thought, agitated.

Then the woman whispered, "God, just let me handle it. You probably shouldn't even watch, anyway. Ken said she runs around the apartment wearing high heels and a thong, and that's it."

There was a knock on my door.

"Who is there?" I questioned, still half-asleep. One of the main advantages of being a call girl is that you get to sleep as long as you like. The self-evident fact is that you don't even have to leave your bed at all if you, for whatever reason, don't fancy it. Being awakened abruptly was entirely aggravating.

"It's me, your neighbor, Virginia."

Drowsy, I opened the door. My neighbors Ken, Richard, and Virginia stood in the hallway gazing at me in my white cotton pajamas with kittens embroidered on them. Ken said "hi" and departed. Virginia advanced into my apartment.

"What's going on?" I asked, curious about this invasion.

Virginia wore the uniform of typical Nevada women: a velour tracksuit, in pink. Her lipstick matched the color of the suit exactly; it was as if someone had painted them both on her.

She said she wanted a word with me. She was a widow, about seventy years old, and worked as a cashier at the Farm House Coffee Shop at the Nugget Casino. Since moving into the Victorian, I had chatted briefly with her a couple of times, mostly small talk, about how cold Reno gets or if anyone had won the jackpot in the casino. All I had revealed about my profession was that I was a writer. Honestly, I don't think that being a call girl is such a big sin, but I would just as soon keep my real identity from Virginia and the other tenants in my building. After all, gossip is cheap and often quite doomful.

So, what it was Virginia had to tell me that was so important, I couldn't imagine. But, when she handed me a plastic bag, containing three joints, I was surprised.

"Present," she announced. "Well, it's actually from Ken and me. We're, you know, dating. We realized we never gave you a welcoming gift since you moved in."

I stared at the bag. It was a startling revelation. I don't want to judge or anything, honestly, but since I had moved into the apartment, I had often wondered where the smell of marijuana was coming from. It never occurred to me that conservative Virginia and Ken smoked pot. And I was almost sure it wasn't Henrik, in apartment number two. Henrik often invited me over for wine. The main reason he liked me coming over, though, was so he could talk about his life back in Poland and his work with the Polish

Intelligence Agency before he came to the United States. But he never offered me any weed.

I had secretly suspected the man from Argentina in number four across the hallway from me. He was a bit of a player, coming home late at night, each time with a different woman on his arm. Anybody but Virginia!

"You didn't have to do that," I told Virginia, who was anxiously waiting for my reaction. The joints were perfectly rolled and neatly positioned.

"I mean, I appreciate it, and everything," I said, perplexed.

"Oh, thank God," she said, her face lighting up.

"Where did you get this, Virginia?" I asked. Suddenly, it occurred to me that I hadn't smoked weed for a seriously long time.

"Oh, don't worry about that. Ken has a very special friend in California who comes by every month or so. It's really good."

When I got over the initial trauma of picturing Virginia getting high, I placed the bag on the coffee table and offered Virginia one of the tasty peanut-shaped handmade chocolates from Ethel M. Chocolates on Plumb Lane that Bob, a client of mine, had brought over the previous day. "Would you like some chocolate?" I asked. "I have a special friend who brought me these."

Like most great pleasures, chocolate is best when it's shared. Virginia grinned and accepted a candy. She sat on the sofa and looked around my apartment.

"My apartment is almost shaped like this one. I like how you use your space," she said. "What are you working on?" she inquired, motioning to my Mac sitting on the kitchen table.

"It's a book," I said, without elaborating.

"You're writing a book? Oh, that's so neat. What's it about?" she asked.

"Hmm, about a Hollywood producer I used to know." I selectively skimmed over some of the details. I was afraid that if

I told her that the Hollywood producer paid me to do shameless things with him, she might die on the spot, literally.

"Oh, like a sex scandal?" Now she was being intrusive. Most writers don't share a piece until it's done. Didn't she know that? I was thinking on my toes now.

I said, "No, not exactly. It's more of a social critique. How Hollywood shaped the culture and the dreams of many Americans."

I really didn't like lying to Virginia, but when you are in a situation where your neighbor, whom you barely know for three seconds, is asking you personal questions, I say lie anyway.

"Oh, thank goodness," she exclaimed, with a big sigh of relief. "You're not another Monica Lewinski. What a trouble maker!" Virginia was really freaking me out. Why did people always have to be so mean about Monica? It wasn't her fault that the president wanted to have no-sex with her in the Oval Office several times. Who did Virginia think she was? Maureen Dowd?

Then she wanted to know why I am single, but thank goodness, I didn't have to oblige her with an answer. My cell phone saved me before I could open my mouth. I picked it up.

"Hello."

"Hi, it's Brian."

I cringed.

This was even worse than waking up at 8 a.m. Brian was a nuisance. A corporate lawyer and my least favorite client; he was so pompous and self-important. When we talked, no matter how important the subject was to me, it was like I never could say anything right. He always denounced or undermined me, as if he knew everything and I could barely think for myself. What a pain.

"Brian. Hi, how are you?" I said, unenthusiastically.

"Fine. Do you have some time this afternoon?"

"Hmmm, listen, Brian, can I call you back in five minutes?" I said.

Virginia got up from the sofa.

"I'm gonna leave," she said. "I just wanted to tell you welcome to the Victorian."

I thanked her and walked her to the door. Then I walked over to the kitchen and retrieved Kenny from the kitchen cabinet. *Maybe I should smoke some weed,* I thought. Then I'd call Brian and tell him that I'm leaving town.

I sat on my sofa and put my feet up. With Kenny curled up beside me, I lit a joint. I smoked half the joint and tried to relax. It had been twenty minutes since Brian's call.

I was sure he would call back.

Every time Brian gets lonely he calls me, which is nearly all the time; because, he claims, his wife wants to have sex with him only once a month. He is almost fifty years old and has been married for twenty-five years. He says he is a hopeless romantic who loves his wife so much that he would never get a divorce.

Other times he jokes that if he had killed his wife when they first met, instead of marrying her, he'd be out of prison by now.

"But," he says, "why should I deny myself? Call girls are cheaper than wives and cost no more than a date."

He is a shining example of a corporate lawyer's ethic at work: he won't let anything stand in his way.

Brian actually believes Hollywood. Like, he really thinks call girls are just down-to-earth girls, like Julia Roberts in *Pretty Woman*, who've lost their way in the big city. Or like Paris Hilton, who, it appears to me, has just lost her way. Brian believes that if a call girl just had a Prince Charming, specifically a millionaire Prince Charming like Richard Gere, then she would immediately aspire to live out the American dream in suburbia, popping out a Range Rover full of kids in no time.

The fact is that, like Brian, Hollywood has a love/hate relationship with call girls. European filmmakers, like French director Jean-Luc Goddard with his *Vivre sa Vie*, or Spain's Luis Bunuel, with his deliciously perverse classic, *Belle De Jour*, always explored prostitution as a manifestation of repressed desire and as an allegory of the capitalist society.

American filmmakers tend to be more idealistic, if not naïve. Especially when they are trying to be hip.

One prostitution myth that evolved in Hollywood was the knight-in-shining-armor scenario in which the hero rescues the heroine from the wicked pimps who enslave her. In doing so, he frees himself from all his unacknowledged inhibitions; this makes for a happy, or at least a clarifying, tragic ending.

The pattern is much the same in *The Owl and the Pussycat*, *Klute*, *Taxi Driver*, and *Risky Business*. Too bad the knight syndrome didn't come to an end with Robert De Niro's killing spree in *Taxi Driver;* we might not have had to endure the demeaning, but vastly popular, *Pretty Woman*.

I thought that Brian, being a lawyer, would have understood why I was writing my story. That it would strike him how incredibly hypocritical it is that people in Hollywood who exploit prostitution, like my former client Sorkin, get a lot of adoration; yet the ones who actually work and know this profession, the ones who actually inspire the creative talents of these writers and filmmakers, do not.

But all he said was, "It happens all the time."

Like, when the pretentious Sting sang: "Roxanne, you don't have to put on the red light."

Did he give her the money he made by belittling her in public for a song? After all, if he didn't, the song should go: "Roxanne, you can put on the red light. Your day's just started, you can go and sell your body to the night."

The money Brian would pay me just wasn't worth my self-respect. I didn't feel like seeing him.

I went back to bed. And rather than calling him as I had promised, I picked up the phone and dialed Amber.

When I started speaking, she knew I was depressed over the way I consider some people to be so brainwashed by the media, like Brian.

"Look on the bright side," she said. "Someday you'll be a famous writer and have your byline recognized by everybody. I wish I had been the muse for *The West Wing* call girl. If I had been," she said, "I would be the one publishing a book and retiring."

If you smoke weed you will understand my developing a slight case of the munchies. I reached for the box of Ethel M. chocolates. Nibbling on the sweets induced thoughts of Vincent, and once he entered my mind, there was no getting him out.

And maybe if I were not a highly paid call girl, I would know how to go after him.

"Maybe I would be better off if I had not been the muse for *The West Wing*," I said.

"It seems to me he would never reject the girl who was the inspiration for a TV character," she said.

"You know you're not desirable when a realtor turns down a freebie with you," I replied, still depressed.

"He didn't turn you down. He was just not after you the way you wanted him to be. You don't want him. You want to be desired by him. There are other fish in the sea," Amber said.

But the only fish I could think about was Vincent. How to go about getting him was the problem, however. The truth was, even though I had known all these high profile clients, I didn't know anything about how to seduce a regular man like Vincent.

"You need to get going with a blog," Amber said, cutting into my thoughts.

I said, "What for? I'm not interesting. People just say I am to be nice."

I must have still been high because after I hung up the phone I got on my Mac and started researching call girls' blogs. And you know what? It worked. I found four popular blogs by call girls that morning and forgot all about Vincent.

Belle de Jour. NY Hottie. Postmodern Courtesan.

Entries by these high-class professionals were amusing, charming, and candid. I was captivated. Blogging has taken a place in the lives of call girls alongside manicures, bikini-waxes, and garter belts, I thought. And this exposure offers Web surfers the chance to get a glimpse of what happens behind closed doors in our world. This was wonderful. A breakthrough of sorts. This was something I had to do.

Oh thank you, Amber, I thought.

She was right about the blog. If Xaviera Hollander brought sex work out of the closet, I think that online journals will spark the enthusiasm of other call girls so that they get on their computers and write and opinionate. Call girls are learning technical skills, yes, but they are also learning that they have a voice online. Even in a small town in the middle of nowhere, a call girl can be heard and people are commenting.

While reading the Postmodern Courtesan blog, I got quite freaked out with one man's comment.

This "religious" blogger talked about how blogging has given another voice to what he called "a new front on the moral assault on the family and society – the acceptance that anything goes." He called the Postmodern Courtesan a "blight to society, the same way terror is a blight on Islam." He said, " . . . she fired another shot at legitimizing her profession as necessary and that for every one of her clients she writes about, there are men and women that end up with destroyed lives, families and communities and that the trail of destruction is as real as any bomb going off anywhere. And no blog can change that."

Why do you suppose this religious blogger went to the call girl's site, anyway?

"I'm writing a blog," I explained to Brian when he called at noon.

"Aaron will be mad as hell when he reads it," he said. Well, at least something positive would come out of it, I thought. *Besides, Aaron won't be the only person who will be upset. So will you, Brian,* I thought. Brian wanted to see me that afternoon.

"I can't. I better take the day off and write," I said. "Things are going so well."

So what if he showered me with nice presents, like Chanel kid-leather gloves. He didn't respect me and had no sympathy for how Sorkin had hurt me. The longer I knew Brian, the more repulsive he became to me. After I hung up the phone, I started to feel better. It felt fantastic turning Brian and his money down. Suddenly I wasn't feeling undesirable anymore.

I wanted to get to my blog. Now, I could actually share the experiences that I'd had with Aaron online. "You want to come over and help me write the blog?" I said to Amber when I called her back.

"Sure!" she said, brightly.

"Good girl!" I said.

"You're going to be famous and forget Vincent so fast you won't even know it," she said, giggling.

As we read articles online about Sorkin, I stumbled upon a Website by another Hollywood producer, William Richert. The article that caught my eye was titled: *Unauthorized West Wing.*

"Oh my God!" I said.

"What's wrong?"

"It's this Website," I said, scrolling down the page.

It stated that in 1995, the executives of Castle Rock Entertainment and writer Aaron Sorkin defrauded writer William Richert of his credit as the original author of the motion picture *The American President*. Also as the original creator of the cult fave TV series, *The West Wing*.

Long before *The American President*, in the mid-eighties, Willam Richert had written a screenplay entitled *The President Elopes*, for Robert Redford's company, Wildwood Entertainment. It was the story about a widowed president with a child who finds romance.

William Richert's original deal with Redford was that he would be paid $50,000 and, once it would be filmed, two-percent of the net profits of the film.

Robert Redford, co-producer with Rob Reiner of the film, then gave Sorkin drafts of the original screenplay, *The President Elopes*, to re-write.

But when the film was made, Aaron claimed to be the original writer of the script and even denied ever having heard of *The President Elopes*.

He used many situations and characters William Richert had created in his original script.

Rob Reiner then paid $5 million to Robert Redford for *The President Elopes*, so they would own the copyright. That done, even if every single word in Sorkin's adaptation had been the same as Richert's original, Richert couldn't sue for copyright infringement because the company Sorkin worked for owned the copyright.

At the time, it was the largest amount ever paid for an original screenplay.

Julia Bingham, vice president of Legal Affairs for Castle Rock Pictures at that time, was engaged to Aaron Sorkin. She later became his wife.

"This was a huge scandal," Amber said, after reading the page.

"I know!" I said.

"Imagine how upset I would be if he would have stolen my entire script," I said.

"Here's William Richert's bio," Amber said, clicking on the link. I read the long list of credits of William Richert's career.

Suddenly, I felt lightheaded. I sat down. I couldn't believe what I was seeing. I snapped my eyes shut and kept them like that.

"What's the matter?" Amber asked. I opened my eyes. As I had suspected, the words were still there. I gasped.

It said:

1977 – WRITER OF "THE HAPPY HOOKER" STARRING LYNN REDGRAVE.

This is just the most incredible thing in the universe, I thought. Can you believe that the same man who wrote the screenplay for *The Happy Hooker* had also had his script stolen by my client?

"Amber, do you really think it's true?" I said. "Well, it's right there on the World Wide Web. Once something's on the Web, it's official," she stated, matter-of-factly. "And as you know, when it comes to gossip I am a believer. Look at it this way, at least you're not the only one Aaron plagiarized. This is more free publicity for you."

"I have to call this guy William Richert," I said.

Amber was grinning. This was getting serious, I realized.

The next day, I e-mailed him.

From: Dimitra

To: William

Re.: Aaron

Dear Mr. Richert,

I had the pleasure of reading your website yesterday. I am sorry about Aaron Sorkin stealing your credit. Did you know that Aaron based a character in *The West Wing* on me?

Sincerely, Dimitra

His response came almost immediately:

From: William

To: Dimitra

Re.: Aaron

I heard. It was the talk of Hollywood during the Television Critics Award in January.

Would you be interested to let me interview you for my website?

Bill

William Richert wanted my story.

He was the man who wrote the screenplay for *The Happy Hooker*, the book that inspired me to become a call girl all those years ago!

I decided that if I was going to give someone all the shameless details of my past with Aaron, I would much rather give them to him than to someone who might be more judgmental, like Katie Couric.

And can you believe, out of all the call girls in the universe, I was the one involved in a major Hollywood scandal? What are the odds of that for a call girl like me? I thought.

Chapter Six

Even in my most imaginative fantasies, I never dreamed I would be backstage at a Madonna concert, give away free sex, and within the same week travel by private jet to meet with a prince from Oman. I really love music, and it plays a pretty important part in my life. And a Madonna show can't easily be topped.

But I was also a Manhattan high-priced call girl with some exceptionally high-profile clientele; and in most cases, the more high-profile the client, the easier it makes my assignments. And there isn't a call girl alive who would turn down a prince. Especially Prince Kalid, of Muscat, Oman. (And yes, he is attractive and speaks English as well as he speaks Arabic.)

So, you see, I was quite dismayed when faced with the dilemma of choosing between Madonna and Prince Kalid; consequently, I did both.

My dilemma started on a beautiful June evening as James, the man I'd met at Roseland, and I sipped frozen margaritas at Arizona 206, the Tex Mex restaurant on East Sixtieth Street.

"Even money can't buy this," said James, eyeing me from over his chilled glass.

The Madonna concert at the Meadowlands was surely the zenith of New York events, although, technically, it was in New Jersey.

"Absolutely nobody gets backstage except a very, very few exclusive celebrities. But you're in," James assured me, handing me a second row ticket and a colorful laminated backstage pass. "I got you on the list."

The pass read:

Madonna
Blond Ambition Tour
Byrne Arena
ALL ACCESS

I could barely believe my eyes. This was the best thing that had happened to me since arriving in New York City.

But, as glamorous and alluring as the opportunity was, I realized I couldn't attend because of work. Why couldn't Madonna have come sooner, or later, than at this particularly scheduled date?

As I sat looking at James and pondering his fabulous invitation, I considered our brief relationship. After James and I had first met a few days prior to this, he had called me every day and asked me to have dinner with him. I had said "no" exactly three times.

But on this day, and with my believing that a man employed by the largest concert promoter in New York City could be good for my career as a photographer, I had agreed to meet him.

But the thing was, I was booked to fly to Las Vegas the following morning to spend two days with a prince from Oman whom I had previously met in New York. The prince had called International Escorts to again request my company.

"Stupid girl," said James, when I told him I couldn't make the concert. "You cannot miss this." He flirted with me all night at the restaurant. He was twenty-eight, charming, and prided himself on having been born and raised in Manhattan. He said he was one of only ten percent of the people living in Manhattan who had actually been born there.

He had worked practically all his life, having started modeling professionally at age six. At sixteen, he started writing songs and singing. Later, he was offered the opportunity to work for entertainment promoter Ron Delsner.

His job was to look after the artists and make sure that they appeared on schedule and that they consummated their contractual arrangements.

He took pleasure in talking about the famous people he knew personally.

He didn't have to work the Madonna show because he was "on a two-month summer vacation," he said. Still he had every privilege imaginable. *How good does it get?* I thought.

"Okay," I finally said. James was very pleased.

I knew I should fly to Las Vegas to be with the prince, but I just couldn't resist the idea of mingling backstage with New York celebrities.

Feeling unbelievably guilty, I called Marie and told her that I wasn't feeling well; therefore, I had to cancel Vegas. Marie believed me because no one passes up a $4,000 check, plus two days in pure Vegas luxury with royalty.

The day of the show, I could barely concentrate on anything. I had become so accustomed to negotiating with men over money that it felt weird to go out with someone who hadn't "bought" my time even though I thought he was kind of cute. And actually, James' telephone calls to me over the past few days had been a great comfort.

I realized that I had become very lonely since Teresa had moved to L.A. Before Teresa left town, we did everything together. We had traveled thousands of miles from home and were close-knit as a family. We used to work and play together.

I guess everybody needs somebody.

Security at a Madonna concert seemed to be tighter than that of the Pentagon. Maybe this country's president should take tips from the star's bodyguards; they certainly seemed to run a tighter ship than the Department of Homeland Security does these days.

Backstage at the Byrne Arena, over one hundred crew members had spent two days assembling the monstrous 70-foot by 80-foot stage that had arrived in eighteen huge trucks.

James and I stopped for an Absolut with cranberry juice at the bar at the far end of the backstage area near Madonna's dressing rooms. With drinks in hand, we mingled with VIPs, including the media, people working for Madonna, Warners, and acquaintances of tour people. Honestly, everybody was like the child of a Beatle or a Pink Floyd.

The glamorous Madonna was followed everywhere backstage by a documentary crew. I heard they even followed her to the bathroom. Maybe it was lucky Madonna had so much security. After all, the Pope had recently condemned her because of the combination of pornography and religion in her shows. It was smart of her to protect herself from certain religious fanatics.

Soon, James and I retreated to our seats to watch the show.

Things got noticeably surreal. Madonna's fans were out of control. They were jumping out of their seats, red-faced and screaming before Madonna even arrived. To me they didn't exactly look like the friendliest group of people. Sometimes I worry about performers like Madonna, I really do. *Poor, rich, beautiful Madonna,* I thought.

"Why didn't you bring your camera?" James asked. He had figured I would be snapping photos by now. "I didn't know I was allowed to," I replied, suddenly noticing millions of photo ops.

"When you are with me, you're allowed to," he said, matter-of-factly. *How cool,* I thought.

As all other Madonna fans, I was unable to stay still or quiet. And, being with a VIP from the music business was by all means more fun than being in Las Vegas with a handsome prince-of-any-country.

The show began with a recreation of the factory set from her *Express Yourself* video.

Madonna emerged on a hydraulic platform wearing the men's suit and monocle she had worn in the video and screamed, "Hello, New York! Do you believe in love? 'Cause I got something to sing about it...and it goes something like this..." and immediately launched into *Express Yourself.*

Her long blonde hair was scooped up in an *I-Dream-Of-Jeannie* ponytail, and she had a triumphant look on her face.

Express Yourself is a song about female assertiveness and empowerment, and Madonna demonstrated this by simulating sex with her male dancers. She removed the suit halfway through the song to reveal an astonishing Jean-Paul Gaultier bustier. She was in her finest form, both vocally and physically. For *Like A Virgin,* she appeared on a huge red bed, surrounded by male slaves who simulated various sexual positions with her. When the men left the stage, Madonna was alone in a simulated masturbatory frenzy.

Spiritual redemption followed with *Like A Prayer,* and the set ended with *Vogue,* followed by an encore of *Holiday* and a medley of *Family Affair* leading into *Keep It Together.*

She went through her set list with so much energy and passion, chatting up the audience and even cracking a joke about vaginas.

Madonna was such a sexy woman and performed the most stimulating happenings that she made even me think about having sex for pleasure. And though I wasn't planning on duplicating any of her on-stage acts for my own self-fulfillment, I found much satisfaction in having James beside me, and sensing his eyes on me.

I think the Madonna show was the reason I felt so extraordinarily turned on the rest of the night. After the concert, I left the theater in awe of what I had just been part of. And James just couldn't stop tempting me with his seductive charm. Knowing how I like sushi, he took me to Sushi Hana on First Avenue. "Not only are they open until 3 a.m., but they also have the best Yellowtail in all of New York," he said, casting an eye at me as he parked his silver Volvo in a tight space on East 63rd Street.

He was so warm and easy to be with. I felt it hard to believe that I had actually panicked the first time he'd asked me out. But, after all, I had not dated since I left Germany. Now, with James and me spending three hours together at the concert and sharing laughs and stories, he was no longer a stranger.

He wrapped one arm around me and his leg was almost touching mine as we walked from the car to Sushi Hana. I felt a strong tingling as my body responded to him. He was confident and self-assured, yet held a tantalizing boyish charm. He was cute, with his green eyes staring at me and with his long blonde hair flowing. He stopped just before the restaurant and before I could say anything, his hands cupped my face and he kissed me on the lips. I did my best to hide the effect he had on me, still, I felt myself blushing. He was so tall that I had to look up to him.

For a moment, we stood there on the brightly lit street, me wobbling into him on the uneven sidewalk in my 4-inch stilettos. I don't know if it was the choppy sidewalk surface or the events of the hair-raising evening, but I found it necessary to grip James' arm for support as he led the way to the restaurant.

I giggled, unconsciously.

"What?" he asked, grinning.

"Oh, nothing. I'm not used to having a strong man to lean on," I joked.

"Lean all you want. It makes me feel useful," he said.

During dinner, I looked long and intensively at this very desirable creature sitting across from me. And he certainly was fixed on me; he even ignored his drink when the waiter set it on the table.

I really was wrapped up in him, too, for as I ate I had no idea what it was. It tasted good, but I suspected anything would have tasted good that evening while in James' presence. He had such a gorgeous smile; and I couldn't get enough of his green eyes as they constantly moved over my face. I tried to read his expression. Did he want to sleep with me?

He was adorable, but I was irritated by my own behavior because I didn't want to come across as cheap or easy.

I desperately tried to think of something else. There was nothing to take my mind off him, though. Suddenly, he stood and took my hand, gently pulling me up.

"I think it's time to go," he said.

I have no idea how we got to his apartment in a classic brownstone building on West 73rd Street on the Upper West Side. But out of the blue, I felt his arms around me.

I felt his lips cover my mouth. Our clothes were gone, and his slender fingers were creeping up my back, and then touching the sensitive skin on my neck. He was turning me on. I couldn't stop now even if I wanted to. I ran my hands through his blonde hair while his hands slid down my bare back to my ass; and then he squeezed it.

"I'm not exactly sure what's happening between us," James whispered in my ear.

"Me neither," I replied.

It was remarkable that something was happening between us. Some guys would never entertain the notion of having a romantic relationship with a call girl. But I didn't think it would matter right now to James because, at the moment, I had no intention of telling him of my profession. There would be time for confessions later.

Rock and Roll parties always make me feel so good about myself, and truthfully, when James started making love to me, I completely forgot that I was a call girl. And he went down on me with so much enthusiasm that one would never suspect he had just recently had sushi.

Of course I freaked out the next morning when I regained consciousness and found I was still in his apartment; actually, I was still in his bed. I was terrified that he would think I sleep around. (And I certainly don't sleep around.)

James was not in bed. I got up and slowly walked around the one-bedroom apartment.

I found him in the kitchen. He had done something really beautiful. He had made breakfast and coffee, and he had placed everything on a tray to bring to bed. It made me melt. He kissed me on the cheek.

"Hungry?"

"I guess." I decided to wait a while longer before telling him about my night job. He stared at me for a moment, scrutinizing my face before handing me a cup of hot coffee.

"What's wrong?" I asked, a bit confused.

"Nothing's wrong. Just – " He paused, looking adoringly into my eyes. "I think I am falling in love with you."

After breakfast, at my request, James drove me to my apartment building on 53rd Street. I took his phone number and promised to call him later. "I can't wait," he said, and kissed me again.

I went upstairs, and as soon as I walked into my apartment, I noticed the message light on my answering machine beeping like crazy. I pressed the button to hear my messages. And without surprise, a familiar voice began speaking.

"Hi, it's Marie. Could you please call me as soon as possible, darling? Thank you."

"Hi, Marie here. Where are you? When are you going to get a pager, darling?"

"Marie again. Please call me. Prince Kalid still wants to see you. He sent his private jet to pick you up as soon as you are feeling better."

"Marie, what's going on?" I said, when I finally returned her calls.

"I've been trying to get a hold of you for hours! Is everything all right? Are you feeling better, darling?" she asked. "The prince would like you to join him in Las Vegas. He even sent his private jet. How soon can you be ready?"

"Umm, an hour, maybe?" It was noon already.

"Good! I'll tell him. He has a limo picking you up at your apartment and taking you to Teterboro. Have fun, and please call me when you get to Caesar's Palace." She hung up.

Teterboro? I really had no idea what that meant. I called Marie back. "Marie, what is Teterboro?"

Pause. Then I heard giggling on the other end.

"Sorry, darling. It's an airport that deals only in non-commercial flights."

Most people, including me, have a weakness for private jets that is so powerful that they simply cannot say no to an invitation to fly. The $4,000 a day the prince would pay me made it even harder to turn it down. However, today I just couldn't stop thinking about James. After all, he was in love with me.

Was I in love with him? It was hard to tell. I didn't know how I felt about him because I had never been in love before and had nothing to compare to what I was feeling.

Right now, this minute, I wanted to call Marie and tell her that I couldn't go, even if it was a sin to turn down the money and the trip on the private jet. I couldn't bear the idea of spending two whole days with a rich, spoiled prince when what I really wanted was to be in the cozy brownstone apartment building doing something insanely romantic with James, like feeding each other breakfast in bed.

I dialed James' number. I would tell him that I missed him and that we should spend the day alone together. I waited, and then his answering machine picked up. His recorded voice on the line was a jolt.

Suddenly, I felt beyond miserable. What was I thinking? Of course I could use the money the rich prince would pay. James could wait. In fact, I told myself, there is nowhere better to contemplate last night's events and what I should do about them than in a private jet.

I got dressed for my trip in red Versace shorts and a white shirt and slipped on a pair of white Chanel flip-flops. The flip-flops were so that nobody would think that this was my first time on a private plane. I didn't want people to think I got especially dressed up for the occasion. The driver buzzed my door at exactly 1 p.m. I grabbed my overnight bag and hurried down the stairs.

A black stretch limo was waiting on the street. I hopped in the backseat. The interior was cool and very soft. The driver explained that I should pick up the phone and let him know if I needed anything. *God, why are they always so nice to you in limos, but so rude in taxis,* I thought. I said, "Thank you," and we sped off. When we arrived at Teterboro, all the prince-connected people were glowing with pleasure to see me. Their smiles were as big as Giant Stadium.

Even non-prince-connected people at the private airport were so nice, I swear. I smiled back at everyone as if to say, "I do this all the time, you know, running to catch a private jet. Just like all the moguls around here."

As I had suspected, there were no check-in lines at Teterboro. There was no waste of valuable time dealing with airport procedures, either. No waits at boarding gates. No baggage lines.

Captain Pete chatted with me while we walked side-by-side from the lobby to the Falcon 900, a tri-engine jet. "Thanks to a third engine you can feel super safe," he assured me, as he explained some of the plane's features. "You know what they say about private jets," he stated. "Statistically, you are safer in one than you are in a car." Pete enjoyed his work, and it showed.

As I sank into the luxurious leather seat of the Falcon, I wondered if other people knew about this plane. Someone needs to tell Continental Airlines about this jet, I thought, because it made a commercial 747 look like a Greyhound bus.

The fourteen-passenger jet was equipped with a refreshment center with snacks and beverages, a full kitchen, TV, VCR, and CD player with surround-sound system and phones and fax-machines. There was a nice collection of CDs and movies in the cabinet. Everything about the jet was gorgeous. I slipped the Pet Shop Boys in the CD player and kicked off my flip-flops.

This non-commercial flight had made me so happy already; I decided to tell James that I was a call girl and that I couldn't see him again. And he should fall out of love with me, because it is impossible for call girls to keep boyfriends.

Maybe he would forget me before my return to New York, which would be very convenient.

"Are you comfortable?" a voice asked.

I was startled. It was Captain Pete.

"Fine, thank you," I said, smiling back.

"If it's all right with you, we can take off," he said.

"Me?" I said, and looked around the plane. Then I said as confidently as possible, "Okay, I think I'm ready." He smiled, nodded his head, and returned to the flight deck.

I don't know who the prince had said I was, but I didn't think the flight crew knew I was a call girl. Captain Pete and Captain Hunter were the kindest people I had ever met in my entire existence. The prince had dispatched them at 4 a.m. Las Vegas time to fly to Teterboro. But the time hadn't mattered at all to them. The prince, their boss, used the jet as ordinary people use a car, they said.

"There is no fixed schedule in his life. We never know where we're flying to next," said Hunter, the taller, younger of the two pilots. "He is a man who does what he likes, when he likes. We work hard, but he works harder." At $1,000,000 a year it costs to maintain the jet, it's no wonder the prince works from 4 a.m. until 11 p.m., I thought.

On our first meeting, the prince had spoken briefly about his homeland Oman.

I find geography and history highly interesting, especially when the information comes from the top leaders of a country. And the Oman prince was certainly at the top.

I learned that the Sultanate of Oman borders the United Arab Emirates at the northwest, Saudi Arabia at the west, and Yemen at the southwest.

From 1891 until 1971, Oman was a British protectorate. The Sultan of Oman has since greatly improved the economic situation of the country and had remained in peace with all the other countries in the Middle East. The royal family of Oman is very small, numbering fewer than one hundred male members. These junior princes, uncommon for a Gulf state, enjoy very few privileges. While some of them hold cabinet and government offices, these are not guaranteed and suitability is judged by merit. In business, the royal family takes pleasure in the luxury of being very well connected, but success comes as a result of their own endeavor. Kalid, thirty years old, ran a 4,000-employee organization in construction and hotel development. He resided in Muscat, the capital of Oman, while many of his business activities and offices were located in New York and L.A. I learned lots about the prince and his country, although, on our first encounter in New York, we had only spent a couple of hours together.

I stepped from the jet into the June 104-degree heat and was met by a uniformed driver of a White Rolls Royce. He introduced himself as Earl. He was to escort me to Caesar's Palace, he said. And then, once we reached the Strip and stopped at the elaborate hotel-casino, a ferociously tanned man in dark pants and shirt, wearing aviator sunglasses, and with a noticeable earpiece, met the Rolls Royce and escorted me to the suite.

Another man, wearing identical clothing and sunglasses, met us outside the suite. The men looked like they had spent all their lives in a gym.

Bodyguards, I thought. How glamorous to have your own special protection. Kalid appeared from the living room and the bodyguards vanished, though I was sure they were close by.

"Lisa," Kalid said, in a welcoming voice. He came closer and gave me a hug. "How was your flight?"

"Heavenly," I answered truthfully. I looked around the decadent décor.

"Kalid, this is – " I stopped to consider what I was about to say. Then I glanced at a long window that exposed the entire neon-lighted city.

"I know," he said. "The suite is a bit much, but it was all they had available."

We were in an opulent two-story penthouse suite, with three bedrooms and five bathrooms.

In the living room, there was a dramatic circular stairway and four eight-foot Italian marble statues of Roman heroes, along with hand-carved gilded furniture. The master bedroom had two cast bronze lions at the foot of the lavish canopied bed. Cut stone arches, marble columns, and handmade mosaic murals occupied the formal dining room.

I felt like Cleopatra and Kalid was the Roman Emperor in the suite. Kalid must have felt Roman, too. Without hesitation, he suggested we both get in the enormous Jacuzzi to relax. While we waited for the tub to fill, Kalid turned on the stereo, opened a bottle of Cristal champagne, and then entered the bathroom with two glasses. He was wearing the fluffy Caesars' bathrobe.

"Now," he said, as we sank into the warm bubbles, "tell me all about your exciting life in New York." He touched the glass to his lips and gazed over the rim to the sparkling bubbles dancing over my breasts.

Chapter Seven

I didn't sleep the entire week after receiving the e-mail from William Richert that was sure to transform my life. He wanted to interview me. A call girl.

This was good. Here I was miles and years away from my encounters with Aaron Sorkin, still, our client-call girl relationship was about to explode.

His having a relationship with me had already been the talk of L.A. at the Critics Awards; any comments at all involving Sorkin would surely glue his fans, as well as non-fans, to the Internet. And William Richert is esteemed in Hollywood and a highly regarded screenwriter.

And to think, I would never have gotten this far if I had stayed with James in New York. I loved James with all my heart, but with his flirtatious ways and my being a call girl, things never would have worked out for us. I owe a lot of thanks to Aaron Sorkin for my not getting married. Had it not been for him, I might never have left James.

It all began while I was in Las Vegas with Prince Kalid. James hadn't called me the entire two days, not once. So, I missed him, but I was glad I'd made the trip in that luxurious private jet that was fit for a king, no pun intended. Could you imagine giving up $4,000 for a man who doesn't even call after spending the entire evening and night with you? (The prince paid $8,000 for my company, but the agency's fee was fifty percent, which means they got $4,000.)

Even though during the flight I had made up my mind to tell James that I couldn't see him again because I was a call girl, I had truthfully expected him to call. The day after I returned from Vegas, he called with an excuse for not having called all weekend.

"I had to drive to Philadelphia and do a show with Bill Cosby," he said. "I was in Philly three nights, and unfortunately I left your number at home."

"Ron Delsner does shows in Philadelphia?" I asked.

"This wasn't for Ron. It was a corporate event for Seagram's at the Four Seasons Hotel. They called at the last minute and asked me. I've organized events for them before," he said.

We chatted about Bill Cosby and then out of the blue, James invited me to spend a few of days with him in the Hamptons. "Come with me to the beach tomorrow. We can stay in my sister's house," he said. He knew just what to say. I forgot, at least temporarily, that James had neglected to call me for two days after our tryst, or maybe I didn't really care.

But the idea of going to the Hamptons with him excited me. I knew that New Yorkers considered the Hamptons the ultimate summer getaway. The setting there is something straight out of a coffee table picture book. Pristine white beaches and vast Gatsby-like homes surrounded by sprawling yards and fences. Historically, its shores have drawn affluent families and successful artists like the famed Truman Capote and Willem de Koenig. And in later years, Steven Spielberg, Robert De Niro, and Lorne Michaels. I had heard much about various areas surrounding the city; and the Hamptons were at the top of my list of places I wanted to visit. Once there, I wasn't complaining; the area was more than I had anticipated. Though sprinkled thickly with elegant shops and restaurants, East Hampton commanded a rustic, small-town feel. The scenery and the serenity were genius.

We stayed at the home of James' sister for an entire week. It was a traditional oceanfront beach house with a very inviting and spacious living room, separate dining room, two bedrooms, three bathrooms, and three fireplaces. It also had a vast porch, a heated swimming pool, and a perfectly manicured garden. And what made the trip more perfect was that James and I had the house all to ourselves. (Maeve, like James' other four siblings, was in the movie business. Maeve was the assistant-turned-wife to a movie mogul at Tri-Star Pictures in New York before Sony bought the studio and moved their offices to L.A. Now she and her husband Ted were on a business trip to the West Coast.)

James and I were in Shangri La. He held my hand while we strolled along the broad stretches of pale sand, passing luxurious mansions and listening to the tumultuous waves of the Atlantic Ocean.

And James was so adoring. Just the way he looked at me turned me on. And when he touched me, I felt delirious. These days and nights with James were bliss. I thought James was just about the perfect man. The more time I spent with him, the more handsome he became, if that was possible. He was so charming and witty, and he made me laugh.

Before I knew it, James and I had become inseparable. It was heaven.

But it was also difficult. He sometimes had a way of looking at other girls that was unsettling. I guess I can say that I was jealous and actually possessive.

As I told my mom on the phone later, because she was super upset that by the summer I hadn't yet returned to Germany, I had fallen madly in love with James.

But still, I was a call girl, and as wonderful as being with James in the Hamptons was, I needed to get back to the city.

Aaron might call, I thought, one Friday night as James and I sipped lemonade on his sister's porch. The next evening we did return to Manhattan. James insisted I have dinner at Café Luxembourg with him and his friends Oliver and Katrina. Oliver, blonde and WASPy like James, was a genius videographer who had directed some of the finest rap-videos on MTV. And Katrina was a professional ballerina for the American City Ballet. Anyway, during our dinner, I didn't really think about whether Aaron might call. We ate, drank, and laughed.

I just enjoyed being with my friends, like a normal girl.

I know this is going to sound totally superficial, but I had gotten really lonesome after Prince Kalid had flown me back to Teterboro; he went off to somewhere glamorous, like Cannes, without me. That's the trouble with jet-setting prince-type men: they have to have a different call girl in every city.

Sometime during the next week, I went to the Wiz and bought a Motorola pager, like the one James used for his job, and like the one Marie had pestered me to get.

This pager would keep me in the loop. I called International Escorts and gave Marie my new pager number. Then I dialed Aaron, and we chatted briefly about my being in the Hamptons for the previous week. Before hanging up, I gave him my pager number so he could get in touch with me whenever he needed to. The truth is, I wanted to spend as much time as possible with James. Still, if I didn't work, I couldn't support myself.

I needed Aaron.

I had convinced James that I was making money by photographing concerts in New York for a German music paper. I couldn't believe that he bought it, but I guess he did.

To keep up my reputation as photographer, I started frequenting concerts at Madison Square Garden or at the Beacon Theater and photographing musicians such as Stevie Ray Vaughn, Bon Jovi, Anthrax, Skid Row, Living Color, and others.

It was surprisingly easy to call the various offices of the record companies and receive press passes, which meant that during the performances I was allowed to stay in the press area in between the stage and the first row with all the other professional photographers. Maybe it was because of my foreign accent, or because there were so few other women photographers covering these shows. The publicity execs at Columbia Records and at Polygram loved me and always put my name on the lists.

It was a great way to practice my skill and to get a nice portfolio at the same time, and it was a lot of fun being at the concerts and the backstage parties.

Once I even got to meet the artist Prince, as opposed to an Arab prince, whom Teresa and I had both worshipped back in Germany – as did everybody else there. Somehow, while I mingled backstage before the Prince show at Madison Square Garden, I got invited to the after-party at Palladium. At the party, I teasingly asked one of his bodyguards, who was sitting at a nearby table, if he could ask Prince to dance with me. The bodyguard just looked at me suspiciously and said, "Why don't you ask him yourself; he's sitting right here?"

And I said, "Because if I did and Prince turned me down, I could never, ever be seen at Palladium again."

He grinned and whispered something in Prince's ear, then pointed at me from their table. After a moment, Prince came to my table and asked me to dance with him. I thought I would die on the spot!

Who would ever have guessed that you could be a call girl and a photographer at the same time? But to do so had been much easier than I had imagined.

Of course, it also meant that I had to sacrifice a lot of easy money I could have earned had I stuck only with my call girl profession. I really only took a client when I had bills to pay. I would disappear into a black hole for days, as James always said after I would reappear.

I still saw Aaron on a regular basis, and I went on assignments for International Escorts sometimes, but I wasn't making nearly as much money as my other call girl friends, like Pamela and Megan.

"Oh, I have a boyfriend, too," Pamela said the first time we met at International's office one afternoon. "It's murder because John doesn't know anything about this job. Sometimes I don't work for, like, three or four days, and then I totally freak out. But then when I am working, I freak out even more because I'm always afraid John will find out."

"I know; me too," I said. "I sometimes can't work for a whole week because I stay over at James'. I want to tell him the truth, I really do. But I just can't."

Somehow, Pamela managed to earn close to $10,000 in one month by only working days while her lawyer boyfriend was practicing for his dad's firm. I can't imagine how Pamela did it though. It seemed to me the clients who spent the most money on call girls, like Aaron, always called at night.

I also heard that Megan, a pretty blonde who was unattached, had made nearly $15,000 in a single month. Megan's theory was that the more clients she met, the greater her chances of finding a prospective millionaire husband, which wasn't as crazy as you might think. I discovered that lots of former call girls acquired their husbands that exact way. "Call girls make the best wives," is a phrase that I've heard repeatedly.

Anyway, after about one year of not working a lot and dating James, he asked me to marry him. Looking back, I really don't know if he actually meant it or if it was just something his family expected him to do. We spent a lot of time with his family. Holidays, birthdays, and vacations were big get-togethers for them. And James was really attentive toward me when family members were near.

James, the baby of the family, was going to turn thirty soon. And I guess the pressure was really on for him to get married like his siblings.

However, he never gave me a ring.

We were visiting Maeve and Ted at their home in Pacific Palisades, after they moved from New York because of the Sony acquisition, when Maeve announced that she was pregnant. Surprisingly, James looked at me keenly and right in front of his mom, his sister, and his brother-in-law, said, "What would you want to have if you were pregnant, honey, a boy or a girl?"

I didn't know how to answer that question. Later, Ted, Maeve, James, his mom, and I went to the Ivy on Robertson to celebrate the news of the baby and after that we all visited the set of *Bram Stoker's Dracula*, producer-director Francis Ford Coppola's movie starring Winona Ryder and Keanu Reeves.

Ted, one of the head honchos at the studios, gave us a private tour of the set and Sony Pictures' substantial offices.

Somehow, on the drive back to Pacific Palisades, the talk turned to Rob Reiner's new acquisition, a script called *A Few Good Men,* by a brilliant up-and-coming young writer from New York.

Oh boy, I know him, I thought. Of course, I acted super-nonchalant; I mean, I didn't want James or his family knowing about my relationship with Sorkin.

Apparently, Ted was excited that his studio was involved in the distribution of the movie, and he and James were frantically discussing which actor they thought should play the part of the young navy lawyer character. Ted said Rob Reiner was thinking Tom Cruise.

After James and I flew back to New York, we got invited to a private screening of *The Doors*, Oliver Stone's movie starring Val Kilmer.

Do you know what's really awesome about private movie screenings? You can watch the movie while sitting in a leather-upholstered lounger, exactly like the ones on a Falcon jet, and you can call your girlfriend in L.A. from your own phone that is attached to the lounger.

I apologized profusely to Teresa for not seeing her while I was in L.A. and told her James had asked me to marry him.

"Are you going to tell him that you're a call girl?" she asked.

"I don't know; it's very confusing," I said, "but I wish you could see this private movie theater." I couldn't even think of telling James the truth.

We were having such a good time together. I couldn't contemplate spoiling it with such boring details of exactly how I got my money.

Being a call girl and having a fiancé at the same time was agonizing. The fact is, having a fiancé can wreak havoc on a call girl's bank account.

Was this the sacrifice expected of a woman in love? I spent feverish nights tossing and turning in my bed wondering whether I should get married to James.

This was beyond stressful because when Marie or Aaron paged me, and I was at James' apartment, I could never return their pages. I would call back a few hours later and say I hadn't heard the pager go off. I could not admit to them that I had a boyfriend and that James might get suspicious if I had called back. They thought I was completely unreliable and got very cross with me.

But I really needed the money. Every time I missed out on a lucrative assignment from International, or I couldn't return Aaron's page, I got so depressed that everything James did started to annoy me. I always used to laugh at James' jokes, but now I was just mad at him most of the time.

How could he be so happy when I could barely afford to pay my rent on Fifty-third Street anymore because I was with him almost every night?

I didn't particularly want to have sex with him anymore, either, and this really worried me because sex with James had been a thousand times better than sex with anyone else.

On top of everything, my mother was worried about my living in New York City and insisted on visiting me on Christmas.

James said he was excited about meeting her, but then he did something that almost made me break off our engagement that very minute.

We were at his friend Oliver's loft in West Village for a casual get-together after Oliver had finished a video shoot. James completely ignored me and flirted with the two models from the production all night long. After we left the party, I refused to talk to him in the car, and I asked him to drop me off at my apartment.

I ended up telling him that it was over, slamming the car door shut, and running upstairs. The next day I ignored James' calls and went on a call for International Escorts. After all, I needed respect, not the run-around I seemed to be getting from my fiancé.

I met a European fashion designer whose clothes were some of the most coveted at Bloomingdale's and who lived in a sprawling Park Avenue apartment that was even more opulent than Aaron's. The designer spent all night watching me model his elegant dresses and suits before having sex with me in the morning.

I returned home with a gorgeous white linen pantsuit, a navy silk cocktail dress, and $1,000 after dropping off the agency's share of the money.

But, even though I was appalled by what James had done, I was still in love with him. We had been together for a year-and-a-half, and I couldn't even imagine life without him.

How could I forget the parties and the movie screenings and the dinners? Everything in New York City reminded me of James.

I finally called him the following week. He said he was sorry for flirting with those models and that he only loved me. I fell for his charming apology and met him at his apartment to spend the night.

The next morning, he cooked breakfast for me, just like he had when we first met. He was adorable, always reaching for my hand and kissing me affectionately.

When I finally told him that I needed some space in the relationship, we both cried. James held me close and said he wanted to spend the rest of his life with me, but his pleading only made me sadder.

If I were going to marry him, I would have to tell him that I had lied to him all this time. I didn't know if he would be able to forgive me.

I knew my mother would arrive in New York City the following weekend. She had divorced my father, finally, and was now happily re-married. I told James this and he agreed to send his company limo to pick her up from JFK, then he would disappear for a few days to let me spend some quality time alone with Mom. So, when she visited, and without James' company and despite the chilling December temperatures, Mom and I went everywhere: the World Trade Center, the Statue of Liberty, the Empire State Building, and almost every museum in the city.

She lived for the Italian restaurants in Little Italy and the Indian restaurants in Mid-town. I really wined and dined her.

Of course, she had no idea that I had been working as a call girl. She believed I made my living as a photographer and only paid $700 per month rent for my Fifty-third Street apartment rather than $1,400. She automatically assumed I would be doing well even though I had not become an engineer, as she had insisted all through my growing up years.

It was fun watching Mom practice her English by watching CNN and talk shows like *Oprah*. And she really enjoyed her time in the city. I invited James over to dine several times. He especially praised the rich German Christmas dinner Mom cooked for us.

After Mom left, I definitely missed her. I got very homesick and lonely in my apartment. I just couldn't bear being alone anymore. Maybe marrying James was the best thing to do, I told myself, but I couldn't marry him without first confessing.

At his brother's birthday party in January, I made the clear decision to tell him about my call girl job. And I would have, I think. But it just didn't work out the way I had planned. The trouble was that Aaron paged me around 10 p.m. I hadn't seen him in over a month, and I just couldn't say no.

I told James I was tired and excused myself, and then rather than taking a cab home, I told the driver to take me to Aaron's apartment.

Aaron was not in a very good mood that night. He couldn't relax, and he barely looked at me. He kept going into his study to place calls to Los Angeles until sometime after midnight. He barely noticed my new lingerie.

I got high with him that night, not because I liked getting high, but because I was desperate not to think about James. I knew that if he knew what I was doing, it would crush him. The thought of hurting him was almost too much to bear. This was worse than I ever imagined life as a call girl could be. I was so upset that night; all the drugs in Aaron's apartment couldn't cheer me up. Neither could the electrifying view from the gorgeous penthouse. There were millions of twinkling lights stretched across the city all the way down to the Statue of Liberty. I left Aaron's apartment at 2 a.m. and went home.

There were six telephone messages from James. I dreaded listening to them – James would never forgive me for leaving the party early.

I collapsed into a tearful depression in my bed.

I couldn't sleep that night. Then something odd happened. At 5 a.m., the phone rang.

"Hello," I said. "Hello, is this Dimitra? It was a woman's voice. "Yes, who is this?" I asked. "This is Brooke. I got your number off James' phonebook."

"Yeah?" I said, perplexed. She cleared her throat. "We – we spent the night together last week. James told me he was single. I didn't believe him. Are you his girlfriend?" she asked, her voice a bit low. "Well, did you just call every number in James' phonebook?" I snapped, in total shock.

"The only other women in there were his sisters and his mother," she said. "I slept with him because he said he was single. I had to find out for myself, you understand?"

Livid, I slammed down the phone and yanked the cord from the wall jack.

This was a tad worse than James' flirting. He had actually made love to another woman. And I had this crazy idea that if James found out about me being a call girl he would be heart-broken.

As much as I wanted to call James and confront him, I just couldn't. I guess I was embarrassed. It reminded me of other times in the past few months when we'd been out together and he would chitchat with some attractive girl, right in front of me. Later, he always said they were just friends.

I had believed him because I had wanted to; but maybe secretly James was a womanizer, a slut – and that is far worse than being a call girl in my opinion.

Maybe until now I secretly had not wanted to know the truth. Now that I knew what he had done I hated him, and I couldn't imagine ever speaking to him again. I never would have slept with those men for fun, I thought, but James could go and have sex with another girl and then tell me that I am his one-and-only. It didn't make any sense.

I met Pamela for lunch at Isabella's on Central Park West. My whole body was aching, but I was glad to get out of the apartment.

"Oh my God, what's wrong, honey?" Pamela said, when she saw my red, tear-stained face.

"It's James. He slept with another girl behind my back, and I can't bring myself to tell him that I know," I said, crying my words. "No way! How could he? If John ever cheated on me, I would immediately break up with him. We do it for money, not because we want to. It's totally different. Listen, come stay at my apartment tonight, and this weekend John can introduce you to his friends. He has a lot of cute friends, and they're all young lawyers. If James doesn't appreciate you, you need to go out and have some fun and stop obsessing about him."

"No thanks, I'll be fine," I said, wiping my tears on a napkin. I knew Pamela was desperate to console me, but I had no intention of spoiling her weekend with my crying attacks.

She was right, though. Sex for money is different from sex for fun. It's business. I mean, I'd rather have no boyfriend at all and spend my life alone and meet exciting men like Aaron than have one like James, who flirts with every girl and cheats and lies.

I went home and didn't return any of James' messages that day. I felt sick. All I felt like doing was staying in bed for the next six years, except that I couldn't stand being alone. By 9 p.m., I decided to put on the killer cocktail dress my client on Park Avenue had given me and go out. I didn't know where I would go, but I couldn't stay at home, either.

Dressed and made up beyond belief, I took a taxi to the China Club, conveniently located only a stone's throw from James' brownstone.

I entered the club unenthusiastically, hoping to see a familiar face, but I didn't recognize anyone there that night.

What was I thinking? I knew I needed to confront James about the girl who had called me earlier. I also knew that I had to tell him the truth about my profession. I decided to walk the one block to his apartment. I rang the bell. Luckily, he was home. He buzzed me in.

He looked at me sternly, but didn't say a word as he opened his apartment door. I walked in and looked him right in the eyes.

"You haven't returned my calls. What's going on?" he said calmly.

"James, we need to talk."

He sat on the sofa and just looked at me, like he hadn't slept with another girl at all. I couldn't believe it. I paced his living room, like an angry tigress, trying to find the words to tell him what I had come to say. That we needed to end our engagement before we hurt each other even more than we had already. I tried to speak, but nothing came out.

Then my pager went off in my purse. I took it out and scrolled through the numbers.

It was Aaron.

That's strange, I thought. I had just seen Aaron recently and it had been such a disappointing event that I didn't expect to hear from him again.

Suddenly it occurred to me that I didn't understand men at all. *What's the use in even talking to James now?* I thought. He was a man, wasn't he? He could just buy sex like all the other men.

I wondered if men see any difference at all between sex they pay for and any other sex. Was there even a difference?

It was obvious to me that until the day we women purchase sex from men the way we purchase a new dress, we will never fully be the equals of men.

99

I didn't know what James wanted from me. I just didn't understand him and he didn't understand me, and the harder I tried, the more obscure he became. I felt numb. I looked at him, sitting there like nothing was wrong, and I suddenly regretted having come over to sort things out.

"Sorry," I said. "I have to use your phone." He handed me his cordless.

I dialed Aaron's number.

"Hello," Aaron said.

"Hi, it's me," I said, trying not to burst into tears.

"Where are you? Can you come over now?"

"Actually, I'm not far at all. I can be there in, say about five." I hung up and headed for my coat, but before getting it on, James grabbed my arm. "Where are you going?" he said, his voice demanding.

"I'm going to see Pamela. She has an emergency. I'll call you later," I said, resigned.

I ran out the door and hailed a taxi. "One-twenty-four Sixtieth Street," I said to the driver. I was beyond the point of caring anymore about what James thought. But the minute I entered Aaron's penthouse, the strangest thing happened. He said that someone named James had just called and quizzed him about how we knew each other. I ran into his study, picked up the telephone, and dialed James' number.

"James, how did you get this number?" I quizzed him.

"I used re-dial. This number came up," he said matter-of-factly.

"You what?"

"You lied to me. You said you were going to see Pamela. How do you know Aaron Sorkin?" He was screaming.

"Stop screaming at me, and stop calling me. I think it's best if we don't see each other anymore," I said calmly, and then paused for a moment. "Good night." I hung up.

Somehow, even I was surprised that I had prevented a potentially ugly scene involving my client and my boyfriend in such a mature manner. I was suddenly very calm. After all, I am a professional. It's my job to satisfy my clients no matter what is happening in my private life. I smiled assuredly at Aaron.

"Don't worry, he won't call you anymore," I said.

Aaron didn't appear the slightest bit fazed by what had just happened. He dimmed the lights and lit the white candles that were scattered throughout his living room.

"I'm not worried about anything," he assured me.

"You're not?"

"No."

Aaron and I stayed awake until sunrise the next day.

That was another of my many trysts with Aaron, I thought, as I sat in my apartment in Reno browsing the blogs of call girls on the Internet. I reflected on William Richert and the interview I would give him. I thought about my book, and I wondered how much the famed screenwriter would want to hear when he interviewed me for his Website.

Chapter Eight

Usually, a girl doesn't meet a prospective Hollywood hotshot like Aaron the moment she becomes a call girl, as I did.

Well, I didn't meet him at the exact moment but soon after. Regardless, when I met him I was very young and extremely naive. Aaron was one of my first few clients. He taught me a lot about sexuality as well as about men. I mean, until I met Aaron, I was inexperienced and had no idea that men crave seduction and foreplay as much as women.

For some men foreplay is relatively simple and easy: the touching of the genitals usually does the trick, but Aaron wanted to be tantalized into submission. For him foreplay was a little more complicated. And that was fine with me, because direct genital stimulation was the last place I wanted to go.

It was important for him to know that we have a connection. I told him that I missed him and that I was thinking about him.

Maybe Vincent's flirtation was as tantalizing to him as prolonged foreplay seemed for Aaron. It would be fun to find out, I thought, but right now, I didn't have time to analyze Vincent's behavior.

My foremost concern was getting to L.A. to give an interview to William Richert.

Without much decision making at all, I put the Hollywood interview ahead of my concerns for Vincent. I mean, after all, Vincent would be in Reno when I returned, he would still be parading the halls, and I'd still have time to figure out ways to seduce him. He would still be looking at me as if he were more to me than my landlord.

Anyway, I was tired of people assuming that my body was my only valuable asset. I was going to publish my book and prove once and for all that there was more to being a call girl than sex and

102

money. The interview was part of my life beyond my looks and what I could do for men.

It was clear that William Richert was my destiny.

Bill and I agreed to meet the following week. (He said I should call him Bill.)

My new resolution was to focus on marketing the book that I had started two years prior. By being an author, I would not be like Virginia, my seventy-year-old neighbor, having to work for minimum wages at the Nugget, getting high and waiting to die. *God, what a life,* I thought.

Everybody living in the Victorian was permanently high, and as much fun as that seemed, it would be so much more thrilling to smoke weed in my own beach house in Marbella or in Bali rather than in a rental apartment in Reno – Vincent or no Vincent.

Bill had done something miraculous with my self-esteem, which you'd expect would have turned rather dented from Vincent's avoiding me.

It was like, one minute I'd earn thousands of dollars by screwing a rich screenwriter or actor, and then the very next minute, I couldn't even give sex away to a realtor. So, thanks to Bill, that would all change now.

I had many things to sort out before traveling to L.A.: my flight, my hotel, my outfit for the interview, and most importantly Kenny's kennel.

I thought about the connection between Bill and Aaron and pondered over how Bill and I had been put through the ringer, so to speak.

It was bad enough that Aaron had used me for *The West Wing* call girl plot and totally forgotten to give me any credit at all. Now, according to Bill, Aaron had stolen a screenplay that he had spent years writing; this, if true, was totally deceitful.

Who would do such a dastardly thing?

Well, I guess I know the answer to that.

I really learned some hard lessons from Aaron, but he learned a few things from me, too. Probably the most important thing was how to develop that popular television call girl character.

Almost every time we were together in his penthouse, he asked me to tell him in minute-per-minute detail about my life as a call girl. I wasn't alarmed at first; who knew then that he was gathering information he'd use to build a very popular character for a television series worth a fortune? You know, almost every client is at least a little inquisitive about what other clients are like. But Aaron asked me to describe in graphic detail what I did with these clients. I think out of every client I have ever met, Aaron asked me the greatest amount and the most vivid questions about my job.

"Aaron, you should write a screenplay about a call girl. I can help you do the research," I joked one night, when he was pumping me for information. "I can't do that," he said sternly, as if I had asked him something completely crazy.

But that didn't stop his questioning. I mean Aaron picked me thoroughly. He always wanted to know exactly what my other clients wanted me to do in bed and what their fantasies were. I usually exaggerated for entertainment purposes, of course.

"What's the most men you were in bed with at the same time?" he asked one night, after we both got high. *One,* I thought. "Five. No, wait. It was six, I think."

The great thing about smoking crack is that you can virtually cook up any story, in a second, and it won't even faze you.

"Did you like it?" Aaron asked. "I loved it. They were stockbrokers. They all took turns on one of the guy's desk in his Wall Street office."

"Did you like it?" he asked again, gently caressing my strawberry red hair.

"Yeah."

"Do you want to go to my study and try it on my desk?"

We went to the study and I sat on the desk. Aaron sat in the upholstered chair in front of me. He ran his hands up and down my sheer black stockings. Then he wrapped my legs around his neck; his face was only inches from my crotch. "Tell me what the six men did," he whispered.

"They took off my panties and started to lick and play with my pussy," I said invitingly.

"Don't take them off yet," Aaron said, his fingers rubbing the lace outlining my pretty thin panties. "Just describe to me what they did."

Unfortunately, Aaron was hardly in New York anymore after James and I split up. He spent a lot of time in L.A. during the filming of *A Few Good Men,* and he announced that he would move to California after the premiere. He was already working on another screenplay, *Malice,* a tale about a happily married couple who wanted to have children but couldn't.

Aaron confessed that he hated the script, but he was being paid to write someone else's story.

Toward the end of the relationship between Aaron and me, say the last three or four times we were together, he didn't pay me at all. He had made it seem like we were on regular dates. He even drove me home in his Mitsubishi SUV because he said he didn't like me taking ghastly cabs. "I like you, you like me. I don't see what the problem is," Aaron had said.

I didn't ask Aaron to pay me those last few times because I wanted him to like me. But actually, giving sex away to a famous person made me feel a little bit like a groupie.

A Few Good Men premiered in New York with a big, star-studded gala. Everyone was there. Pamela and I attended the premiere with two tickets HE had sent to me. That I was screwing the writer was the evening's best-kept secret.

Though he sat only two rows in front of us, he didn't see us. He was very busy talking to Rob Reiner all evening, and I didn't want to be rude and impose on him. As far as I could tell, he was dateless.

"What happened to his fiancé," I whispered to Pamela.

"Look at him," she said. "He's gorgeous and successful. Why would he need a fiancé if he can just pay for companionship?"

I must admit that I had an unbelievable crush on Aaron, but I couldn't tell anyone. It is a big no-no for a call girl to have a crush on a client.

With every client I met, I was looking for another Aaron Sorkin. Some came close but just didn't add up.

For instance, I met a hot, young film actor from L.A. through the escort agency who was more beautiful than the most beautiful girl I had ever seen. After our first encounter, he called the agency three times and asked for me during his six weeks of filming in New York. He paid for me to spend nights with him in his suite at the Ritz-Carlton on Central Park South.

He had a tremendous expense account, but I couldn't enjoy anything. He was too endowed and the sex was too painful. He was at least eight inches long.

Though a woman's vagina is stretchy and can take in a wide penis, it can only do so much with one that is super long. You girls know that the vagina is only so long; and an extended hard dick pounding into that tender cervix wall hurts a lot. I want you to know, it's really hard to pretend sex is fun on these agonizing occasions. I wonder why it is that some guys with long penises are so full of pride?

A Few Good Men made Aaron very famous. Soon after the premiere, he left New York for good and moved to L.A. I was heartbroken, of course, but thank God I didn't need his money anymore.

Like most call girls, I always wanted a sugar daddy – a wealthy man to pay all my bills and buy me anything I desired.

Let me warn you, you should be careful what you wish for because often you get it.

Anyway, an older gentleman, Mel, whom I had met as a client through the agency after James and I split up, wanted to be my sugar daddy.

I didn't agree immediately. Mel was sixty-five; I wasn't even twenty-five. There were more than forty years between us. He was so old fashioned it was criminal. The only restaurants acceptable to Mel were La Cote Basque, Le Cirque, and the restaurant at the Four Season's hotel.

Mel's offer to be my sugar daddy sounded too good to be true. What in the world would we talk about? I mean, the few times we'd met, he couldn't even have intercourse with me because in those days there was no Viagra.

Because of his age, combined with his blood-pressure medication, Mel could never have an erection. I ended up giving him hand-jobs each time, and he seemed perfectly happy. Maybe he just liked me for the German lessons, I thought. Actually, his German was quite good.

After my relationship disaster with James, education and career goals became very important to me. I sold several photographs I had taken of a Bon Jovi concert and Keith Richard's birthday party to a British agency. I was very serious about pursuing my career in photography.

And I don't know if it was because Aaron had let me read his screenplays on his Apple computer or because I had been high on crack cocaine, but I seriously thought it would be fun to study screenwriting, too. I enrolled in an evening course at Hunter College.

Mel was way too conservative for an artistic girl like me. During his twenty years in the United States Army, he had attained the rank of Lieutenant Colonel. Later, he attended Harvard business school and graduated in the top one percent of his class. He later taught economics at the Military Academy at West Point. He had served as a battalion Commander in Vietnam and in Germany. After retiring from the military, he started a second career as Chairman of an international sporting goods manufacturing company.

Mel was so besotted with practicing German with me that he offered to pay my rent and my bills, as well as give me a nice cash allowance. All I would have to do, he'd said, was spend three nights a week with him while he was in New York.

He was married, and he and his wife owned a sprawling mansion in Scottsdale.

Of course, Mel hardly spent any time in the mansion with his wife. He claimed that the only reason he didn't get a divorce was because it would cost him $50 million.

Mel lived in a grand apartment building on 54th Street, off Fifth Avenue. From Monday through Wednesday, he worked in his New York office, Thursday and Friday in the office in Maine, and on Saturdays and Sundays, he played golf in Scottsdale.

I think Mel's wife saw him only a few hours each week. How he had the energy to be a sugar daddy with such a fierce travel schedule, I know not.

After a week of considering his offer, I dialed his office in New York. His secretary picked up. I asked if I could speak with Mel. After a short pause, he came on the phone. I snapped to attention.

"Hi. I would like to talk to you about your offer," I said, trying to sound very business-like.

"If you have time this evening, we can meet at my apartment," he said. "I'll have dinner delivered from Le Cirque."

I agreed to meet him at 6 p.m. I called Pamela while I was getting dressed for Mel. "Hey. You'll never believe it. I think I found a sugar daddy."

"Omygod, it's so great!" she squealed.

"I'm not one hundred percent sure yet," I told her, "but I'm meeting him tonight to discuss the terms and conditions."

"Just make sure that you get it in writing," Pamela insisted.

I was shocked. Until now, I had been under the impression that men who were sugar daddies wanted to keep everything secret, but Pamela told me that some of the girls she knew with sugar daddies actually had written and notarized contracts. I laughed and said I would tell her how everything went later.

I seriously wondered how exactly you take a sugar daddy to court if he breaks his contract.

I went to Mel's apartment.

"How much money do you need every month?" he asked. I told him. At least I would be able to stop working for the agency. Now I could be a full-time photographer, I thought.

"Are you able to travel with me on business to Europe and Asia?" he continued.

"It depends," I said. "I have classes at Hunter College on Mondays."

"Okay, so you can be away any other day but Monday?"

That was how I found myself in Paris a few days later. We stayed at the Hotel George V. Surprisingly, Mel fit in well with all the hundred-year-old guests in the hotel.

I must have been the youngest person those hotel walls had ever seen. Honestly, that place should be a museum of history.

Mel pretended he was having business meetings in Paris but between you and me, it was because in Paris he could freely stroll the avenues hand-in-hand with a very young lady who wasn't his wife – me. He could publicly kiss me at the bar of The Ritz, whereas in New York he couldn't because he knew so many people from New York's elite society who also knew that his wife was his age, rather than barely twenty-four.

He was embarrassed to do that in New York, but he wasn't embarrassed to do that in front of promiscuous Parisians.

So, over the next three years, Mel changed my life forever. I wore so much Gucci and Chanel while he was my sugar daddy that I still have difficulty today putting on a pair of jeans to walk to the mailbox. For three years, I rode everywhere in limos and on the Concorde. Meeting Mel was an education in world travel. With him, I stayed at the finest hotels and resorts in the world: The Breakers in Palm Beach, the Dorchester in London, the Raffles in Singapore, the magical Aman Resorts in Bali. We visited Bali six times in three years.

He said when his wife died he would marry me.

"She's the only person standing in the way of our bliss," he would say. The idea of marrying him was enough to make me physically ill. It wasn't just that he was so much older, or even the hand-jobs, or that he was too traditional. He had this particularly disgusting fantasy that he wanted to play out practically every time we were in bed together. He wanted me to pretend I was a thirteen-year-old virgin and he was my first lover. It was hideous.

No wonder he wants me to travel with him, I thought. *He's afraid when he leaves town I will report him to the authorities as a pedophile.*

110

I couldn't sleep at night. I didn't tell anybody about how twisted Mel really was. All my friends thought that I was so lucky to have a rich man take care of me.

"Oh," Teresa said, sighing as she observed my goodies when she visited me in my new loft in Soho. She had graduated from the Pasadena's Art Center and was now working for MTV in New York. "He bought you a Lexus? A Bang & Olufsen stereo? An Apple computer? How fabulous."

"I know, but really it's not as great as you'd think. Trust me."

"Why not?"

"Because he is so bossy and controlling," I said.

"But he is only here three days a week," she said. Three days were for me what three months would be for another woman. And the four days he was away seemed more like four minutes. He would call me almost every day to inquire about what I was doing. It was brutal, really.

I was under terrible stress trying to become a professional photographer; the only other alternative, it seemed, was to marry an old pedophile. I enjoyed the money and the luxury, of course, but I didn't want to go back to being a call girl.

The relationship with Mel became very tense. I was exhausted from all the traveling and shopping and dining at famous restaurants. If I'd known having a sugar daddy was this tiring, I might have chosen someone with a more interesting personality than a sporting goods tycoon.

If there's one thing I'd learned from Mel it was this: there is more to life than spending money. When Dominique, a young fashion model in my apartment building, asked me to take some fine arts photographs of her for her portfolio, Mel freaked out.

Actually, Mel was opposed to girls with serious careers. He thought working destroyed women's sex-drive. He couldn't even bear eating dinner alone that night.

"I'm not supporting you so you can take pictures of models all night."

"Mel, she is paying me two hundred fifty dollars," I said, when he called.

"I don't care. I'll give you the two-fifty. Just come over."

"But it's ten o'clock. You have to get up to fly to Scottsdale in six hours."

"Just come over," he insisted.

I took a cab to Mel's apartment. But God, he just kept on whining. "While I'm in New York, I want to spend as much time as possible with you. You can do anything you want the rest of the week."

I didn't say anything. It was as if I was suffocating. Whenever Mel and I were in a room together, he would suck all the oxygen out of it and I felt as if I couldn't breathe. Mel and I had been together for three years. Now I wondered if maybe I should leave him and go back to International Escorts.

The thought didn't warm my heart. There was no way I was going to pay $3,000 a month rent out of call girl monies.

The next day, after Mel left for Scottsdale, I met with Dominique to look at her photographs. She said she was flying down to Miami that night to work Fashion Week on South Beach.

"I'll go with you," I said.

It was April, and my complexion was paler than that of Michael Jackson. I packed my bag and called US Airlines. Dominique and I took a taxi to La Guardia.

South Beach is an international playground and the embodiment of excess, offering non-stop nightlife, sandy shores, and unique architecture. When imagining the South Beach scene, think Baywatch with an art deco twist. The crunchy white beach stretches up the Atlantic for miles. The city is a melting pot of every nationality on the planet and has been profoundly affected by the Cuban population. It's all fun and sun in Florida. For once I wasn't thinking of Mel and his money, nor how I would survive without him.

Instead of brooding on my sad life in a golden cage, I decided to be positive and enjoy the beach and the parties in South Beach. Just as I was strolling the boutiques on Lincoln Road looking for something to wear that night, I spotted the most heavenly creature I had ever laid eyes on. A tall, dark-haired, green-eyed boy was checking me out from the other side of the street. I stood stock-still and watched his reflection in the store window.

He crossed the street and in an English accent asked if I had a light for his cigarette. He looked like the male version of Catherine Zeta-Jones. He said his name was Alexander and that he was from Wales. He was in Miami studying fashion. No wonder he looked like Catherine Zeta-Jones. She was from Wales, too.

I gave him my lighter and he lit his cigarette.

"What are you doing later?" he asked.

"I don't know. I'm here with a girlfriend," I replied.

"You want to go to Bash with me tonight? I heard that they have the best DJ in South Beach," he said.

"Sure, why not," I said. "I think Dominique's coming, too. I can meet you there."

I gave Alexander the phone number of our hotel and said goodbye. I went in the boutique and bought a gorgeous Vertigo dress. Then I hurried back to our hotel to take a nap before the long night. Parties in Miami last until noon the next day, so if you are going to one, you'll need to nap first.

I woke up at six p.m. Dominique hadn't yet returned to our room. The fashion show had been over since three. I wondered what happened to her.

"Dominique," I said, when she called the room at eight. "I've been worrying about you. Where are you?"

"Ooo-hh," she yawned. "On Star Island somewhere. It's so much fun. What are you up to?"

"I am going out to Bash at midnight. Everyone said it's the club to go to."

"I know! I'm going with these people. They're the fashion designers I did the show for today. Don't ask me their names 'cause I have no idea. I'll see you at Bash later."

I found Dominique as soon as I entered Bash. She was the girl in the shortest dress and was surrounded by four middle-aged men. It seemed that all the models on South Beach were drinking champagne at the bar and ignoring the men. I roved the club looking for Alexander, but I didn't see him anywhere. I sat at the bar with Dominique and the guys and tried to have a good time. Dominique looked highly bored. Everywhere you looked guys with diamond-studded Rolexes were hanging on beautiful girls and buying them champagne. They reminded me of Mel.

All of a sudden I felt a hand on my back. I turned. It was Alexander. I was madly excited to see him. We immediately left Bash together, and I spent the rest of my trip with him in his chic apartment on Ninth Street, courtesy of his parents' family fortune. God, I loved his English accent and his long dark hair.

Back in New York, all I could think about was how I could leave Mel and move to Miami and live near the beach like Alexander.

I had learned first-hand that this sugar daddy thing could really upset a girl's social life. As profitable as it was, I just wanted out –

far away from the sugar daddy prison and away from the call girl business.

I shipped all my furniture and clothes down to Miami on a Saturday morning and before anyone knew what was going on, I had moved into a studio apartment only steps from Alexander's. Freed from Mel's pestering attentions, I jumped right into a new life. I didn't even say goodbye to Mel.

At age twenty-one, Alexander loved that I was older than him, and he loved that I had just given up my entire livelihood in New York City to move to Florida.

Do you know what a huge self-esteem boost it is to do shameless things with a twenty-one-year-old after three years of giving hand-jobs to one who was sixty-eight?

I felt that I didn't have a choice but to tell Alexander the truth about Mel and about my being a call girl. I certainly didn't want another James-like relationship disaster.

Alexander said, "You don't have to work as a call girl. You have the most beautiful body and you can be a stripper and make just as much money dancing."

The great thing about really young men like Alexander, as opposed to old ones, like Mel, was that they actually think it's cool if their girlfriend is a stripper, or even a call girl. It makes you more attractive to them if you're a "ho" – not less.

Alexander used to come by Club Madonna on 15th Street where I went to work four nights a week. He would sit in a plush round chair by the stage and stuff dollar bills into my garter.

"You're so sexy," he would whisper in my ear. "Oooh, I love you!" I'd whisper back. He had to be cautious of his attention toward me to prevent Leroy, the owner, from finding out that he was my boyfriend. Boyfriends just weren't allowed at Madonna's.

It didn't take long at all for me to become a most desired dancer and fit right into the life of stripping. Most strippers have a thing about tattoos. It is so overwhelming that they simply cannot say no when it comes to having colorful dyes painfully etched into their skin. A month or so after starting work at Madonna's, I became part of that particular group.

Today, when I glimpse the butterfly fluttering just an inch above my pussy, I am reminded of forfeiting a sugar daddy with gazillions of dollars to become an exotic dancer. But I have no regrets about it.

None.

Zero.

I've told you enough about my sugar daddy days; now, let me get back to my upcoming trip to L.A. where I would fuel a bold scandal.

I booked my flight as well as one week at the Beverly Hilton Hotel. I called the kennel to book a place for Kenny.

Leaving him was always very difficult for me. I always see those books about how to train cats not to get separation anxiety when their owner has to travel. I wish there were books about training the owners not to have separation anxiety from their cats. How miserable it suddenly seemed to go to L.A. without Kenny. I glanced over at him lying quietly on the sofa. He was staring at me as if to say, "How dare you?" Kenny and I belong together. I am sure of it, and he knows it, too.

But the trip to L.A. was a good idea. It would help my career as a writer. And it would take my mind off Vincent. If I stayed in Reno, I would just start obsessing about him again. Still, Kenny in a kennel was hard to think about. There had to be some other way.

I knocked on my neighbor Henrik's door. Maybe he could baby-sit Kenny while I was gone.

"Henrik, could you watch my cat for a week while I'm in L.A.? I'm leaving at five tomorrow," I said.

"Why are you going to L.A.?" he asked.

116

"I am being interviewed by a famous director about my book," I replied.

"Be careful," he said, raising his finger dramatically. "Hollywood is more corrupt than the KGB. They may even kill you."

I was shocked. How did Henrik know this? Until now, I thought only Bill and I knew about the criminal syndicate in Hollywood.

"It's the only option I have for my career," I said.

The next day I knocked on Henrik's apartment door at 2 p.m. I handed Kenny, his food, litterbox, and toys over to Henrik and gave him my cell number.

I locked my apartment and took a cab to the airport. As great as the trip sounded and as much as I wanted to do the interview, I couldn't bear the idea of spending seven nights without my cat. Suddenly, tears filled my eyes and I was so sad. "Are you okay, Miss?" the cab driver asked. He was eyeing me in the rearview mirror.

"I'm fine," I said.

"Sure?" he asked, concerned. I nodded.

"Which airline are you flying?"

"American," I said, staring out the window. We arrived at departure and I paid the cab driver.

Just when I was checking in at the counter, I thought of Henrik's stern, disapproving face and how he'd warned me not to cause any trouble in Hollywood. I hadn't even mentioned to him about how Aaron Sorkin and I had smoked crack together. Why did he automatically assume I was in some kind of danger? Had Henrik developed a sixth sense by working for Polish Intelligence? Did he know something I didn't?

Anyway, I was going to give the interview. There was no turning back now.

Later, as I was walking toward the lounge for people traveling to L.A., my cell phone rang. It was Amber.

"Hey! Are you excited about meeting William Richert? What time are you getting there?"

"I'm a little nervous. I wish you were going with me," I told her.

She said, "Can you believe Aaron's making that movie about Charlie Wilson and the biggest CIA covert operation in the history of this country? When's it coming out?"

"I don't know. Next April, maybe?" I said.

"Are you okay?" Amber asked.

"I'm great," I replied.

"Are you freaked out about pissing Sorkin off?" she asked.

"I'm a bit freaked out, I guess. What's he going to do to me?"

"Nothing! Try not to think about it. He can't do a thing to you. Call me after the interview."

"I will."

"Bye," Amber said and hung up.

Just as I passed the newsstand, I thought I caught a glimpse of a familiar figure.

I stopped to get a better look. Vincent was here at the airport buying a *Time* magazine. Oh God, I didn't want him to see me. I hate chance encounters, particularly with someone I'm hung up on and trying to get out of my mind. Even worse, I suddenly found that Vincent was way, way cuter than I had realized. The shock made me almost drop my carry-on bag. Suddenly I felt embarrassed. I turned and walked in the wrong direction. Then I thought, how silly of me.

I was just taking a flight to L.A. like a normal person, not at all like someone who was going to give away Sorkin's secrets. Maybe I should just say "hi," I thought.

"Hi!" I called out.

There. It wasn't hard at all. So what if he wasn't after me like all the other men. I didn't care in the slightest. Vincent turned and looked at me. God, I think I turned bright pink.

"Oh, hi," he said, shyly. "Where are you going?"

"L.A. You?"

"Phoenix. I'm visiting my mother. Hey, let me walk you to your gate. It's right next to my gate."

Please God, no! It's one thing to be hung up on someone. I mean he never has to know, right? It's quite another running into him when you're about to disclose your affair with a Hollywood producer. I was tense. Vincent sauntered over.

"What are you doing in L.A.?"

I didn't know what to say.

"Are you okay?" asked Vincent, looking concerned.

"Great!" I replied.

"Really?" he asked, as if he didn't believe me.

"I'm fine. Everything's perfect. I'm flying to L.A. on an assignment."

We headed toward the gates. I was freaking. I mean, I couldn't imagine how I was going to tell Bill that I used to get high with Sorkin without Sorkin getting very, very pissed at me. I suddenly didn't want to fly to L.A. after all. I would turn back whenever Vincent left. In the meantime, I tried to chat with Vincent as if everything were as perfect as I was pretending it was.

"I'm glad you are doing so well with your writing," he said.

"Yeah, I'm doing great! It's really incredible," I lied. I guess I'd really done a number on him. He was totally in the dark. He didn't have a clue what I was really up to. None of my landlords ever did, by the way. We arrived at Vincent's gate. Vincent turned toward the long line. I'd done great.

"Good-bye," I said breezily.

"Have a safe flight," he replied.

"Thank you."

He had absolutely no idea about anything. I turned around and walked to the bar. *There's no way I'm going to L.A.,* I thought.

Having made a conscious decision, I ordered a coffee with a shot of Bailey's. I felt miserable. As I was sipping my Irish coffee and wondering what I was going to tell Bill, I heard a familiar voice.

"Are you planning to miss your flight?" Vincent was back. What was wrong with him?

"Yeah!" I snapped.

"Why would you want do that?" he asked.

"I can't tell you that."

"Why not?"

"Because," I said, a huge tear rolling down my face.

"Are you okay?" he asked. I didn't care anymore what Vincent thought. I had lied enough to him already. "Well, if you really want to know, I was going to L.A. to give an interview about a lying person in Hollywood, but the last minute I chickened out. I'm a pathetic wimp," I cried.

"Did that person hurt you?" he asked.

"Well, if he hadn't hurt me, I wouldn't be talking about him, would I?"

"Then you have to get on that flight," he said. "Come on," and he rushed me back to my gate as the last passengers were boarding for Los Angeles.

"Go on," he said, pushing me toward the door.

"Thanks, Vincent. Have a safe flight," I said, still embarrassed.

"I will. Just stop saying that you are a wimp, okay? Go to L.A. and do what you have to do."

Smiling, I walked onto the aircraft feeling like a million dollars. *Bill, get ready,* I thought.

Chapter Nine

I settled into my seat on the aircraft and pulled a small spiral-bound writing pad from my purse. "Aaron Sorkin," I wrote. He was the reason I was going to California to meet with Bill. And our relationship that began and lasted several years in New York City and was later renewed via e-mail while living in South Beach.

This is how Aaron reappeared in my life:

Whenever a new club opened in South Beach, which was just about every week as far as I could tell, the whole town got really psyched. Everybody who had been partying at other establishments every night suddenly acted as if they had never been inside a club before. It seemed the whole beach population moved on to the new club.

Most nightclubs were populated with super-slim models and middle-aged men in Zegna suits who were determined to sleep with them, or to at least be seen with them. The atmosphere was loud, wild, and sweaty.

After I'd moved from New York to South Beach, Alexander and I attended the opening of a new club on Washington Avenue.

Risk was an elaborate, retro-inspired New York-style club with lounges and even a public shower where people could cool off whenever they felt like it. During construction of this marvelous place, fiery red opalescent mosaic tiles had been set across the ceiling and on the floor on one side of the facility where the shower was installed. Risk was the talk of South Beach, and it seemed everybody wanted to be there when it opened. They were. They couldn't help themselves.

The place filled in the first minute. When Alexander and I arrived, the club was so crowded with middle-aged men and models that you could barely move. I think the middle-aged men were there for the models, who really didn't even notice them.

Alexander looked so good; he wore white linen pants and a dark red silk shirt. And I can honestly say that I looked hot in a black mini-dress and metallic gold sandals. As soon as we pushed our way inside, Alexander got us an Absolut with cranberry juice. We then found a place to sit on a red velvet sofa near the main dance floor.

"Baby, I want to get some ecstasy here tonight. Will you do it, too?"

"No, thanks," I said.

I had once tried ecstasy in New York a couple of years earlier. The next day when I looked in the mirror, I thought I was Michael Jackson performing in the video *Thriller*.

This was certainly not a good look for a dancer or the girlfriend of a gorgeous twenty-one-year-old Welsh boy. I'm not a vain person, but dating Alexander was like being in a Calvin Klein ad. I started to feel an enormous desire to look Calvin Klein-ish myself. Ecstasy had not made me feel as good as people always said that it would.

We had only been at Risk for a minute or so when I saw Sidney, a very busty and pretty dancer from Madonna's, standing on the side of the dance floor talking to a young blonde guy. Her long auburn hair was shining from color to color under the flashing disco lights. I waved her over.

"Hi, baby," she said, when she sat down next to me. (It seemed everybody called everybody baby.) "I totally didn't go to work tonight because of this party. Leroy is going to kill me."

"Why didn't you just tell him you were sick or something?" I asked.

"I can't talk to him. I make so much money for that club, if I called to say I was sick, Leroy wouldn't care anyway. He'd yell at me and threaten to fire me. Anything to make me come to work. Of course, he would never fire me. That's just the way he is and I don't need the aggravation. I'd rather just show up there tomorrow night," she said with a giggle.

"It's my night off," I said. "I'm here with my boyfriend. He went to the restroom," I lied, looking around for Alexander.

"I'm here with my boyfriend, Shawn," Sidney said. "He's a professional surfer and lives in Laguna Beach, California. He's cute, but we couldn't live together. I need my independence."

"I know what you mean," I replied. "I love Alexander – " I stopped mid-sentence. It had been almost twenty minutes since Alexander went on his ecstasy-hunt. I was beginning to worry some. I sure hoped he wouldn't get in any kind of drug-purchasing trouble.

Although Sidney had been known to smoke the occasional joint before work, I didn't want her to know my boyfriend did more drugs than the norm. We're mostly talking weed. Ecstasy was a bit more.

Luckily, though, I didn't have to explain anything. Alexander reappeared through the crowd and interrupted our conversation.

"He-e-e-y!!! Where is my honey?" he shouted. He hugged me and sat down between Sidney and me. Sidney looked bored, but Alexander's face was pink with excitement.

"Q-Tip," Alexander said dramatically, as the DJ started spinning the latest hit by A Tribe Called Quest. "He's a genius!" Alexander started rapping the words of the song as if he were in a karaoke bar; he knew every word.

"Q-Tip and Guru are the two most intelligent emcees out there. East coast rap is definitely superior to West Coast rap. Dr. Dre and Snoop are good, but compared with Tribe or Gang Starr they sound juvenile."

"Enough already, Alexander," I said, exasperated. "You're from Wales. You don't need to participate in the East Coast versus West Coast rap war."

"You're so boring. That's it. I'll be on the dance floor where people appreciate music." He huffed and got up, leaving Sidney and me there. He must have gotten hold of the ecstasy because he was acting like a demented puppy.

Sidney slid closer to me. "They're good in bed when they're so young, but they're so dumb," she said. "I better go look for Shawn. See you tomorrow." She disappeared into the crowd.

I sat there by myself and really listened to the music and the lyrics. It was good. Not only did I get a feel for the music, but I also paid close attention to the DJ. He was quite talented.

I couldn't get over how fast he changed the records and how cleverly he used two turntables. His hands were like magic manipulating the records. It was engrossing to watch him work.

Right then I felt an inexpressible pain inside me; something was about to happen, and I knew it would bring both fear and joy.

According to P. Diddy and a lot of other rappers who should know, hip-hop started in Africa thousands of years ago, but for me it has always been the DJs who made rap entertaining.

And this DJ had to be the cream of the crop. I walked to the booth where a dozen models in miniscule mini-dresses crowded at the door watching the DJ. He would quickly pull vinyl records from two giant plastic crates, spin around, and put them on the turntables. Then he would replace the two previously played records in the crates – all in about two seconds while he kept his body moving to the music.

To me, DJing looked like enormously hard work. Not nearly as simple as it sounded, that was for sure. And it had the mysterious ability to hypnotize the hundreds of bodies on the dance floor. I watched in awe. Suddenly I saw Alexander. He was dancing with a short brunette in a man's white shirt and skintight leather pants. She couldn't have been older than eighteen.

"Alexander. Hey Alexander," I called several times. He didn't hear me. I gave up and left the nightspot alone.

Alexander and I were not well suited, I thought, sadly. I would have to break up with him.

He was a pretty face that blended in perfectly with all the other pretty faces there.

That is the problem with places like South Beach where everyone's drop-dead gorgeous. There are so few unique people that physical beauty becomes tiresome. It's nice to have a boyfriend who looks like a male model, but I found myself thinking that with so many other men that looked like models there, I could find a replacement for Alexander if I wanted to.

This thought worried me. I suddenly felt as superficial as Pamela Anderson. I felt ashamed that all I had ever pursued had been money and beautiful objects, like clothes and furniture. I thought about my argument with Alexander over rap music. I had not liked it because it wasn't what I considered beautiful, and I had failed to see what Alexander saw in it. Obviously, rap was powerful. It was drawing people from every race and economic group, but it really had been created from violence and despair, two things I knew very little about and had never experienced.

How did Alexander and the other rich white kids relate to the gritty lyrics? I wondered. Rap stars like Dr. Dre couldn't move out of the ghetto fast enough, but the white middle class were talking about places like Compton or the Bronx as if they were discussing the French Riviera. I didn't get it at all.

Maybe rappers channeling their anger and aggression into this art form became an expression of self and helped curtail gang violence, but what did a rich white kid from Wales, like Alexander, have to be so angry about?

I knew a bit about music. I had been in the D&D Studios in New York City. At that time, DJ Premiere from Gang Starr had invited me to watch him record a song, but from what I saw, nothing in the studio looked anything like the Bronx. Even the graffiti mural in the foyer, which was expected to set the scene, appeared too slick to be real graffiti like you would see on the outside of a building in the Bronx.

The real art in graffiti is not really the art at all. Not getting caught by police or killed by a rival gang is the real art in painting graffiti. The absolute meaning of it is that the artist marks his territory, pissing off both police and rival gang-members. The artist who had painted the studio's graffiti had none of these concerns. Security at D&D was fierce.

DJ Premiere was a well-educated sweet man who could hardly harm a fly. He was surrounded by millions of dollars' worth of recording gear, drum machines, and laptops. Nothing about him or his music suggested violence. His partner, Guru, had been known to occasionally rap about violence, but he too was so highly educated, it seemed like a joke when he shot out the lyrics.

I couldn't understand how Alexander and other people could try glamorizing ghetto life. I needed to find the answer.

The next day, I started talking with Leo, Club Madonna's DJ, and a few of the dancers who always performed to hip-hop music. I discovered that hip-hop wasn't at all about the ghetto. It wasn't even African-American.

"Hip-hop," said Leo, "is emceeing and break-dancing and scratching records and graffiti. People from every society and culture respect hip-hop. Not all the Godfathers of hip-hop were black. The first break-dancers were Hispanic, and the first graffiti artist, Taki, is a Greek."

"So, hip-hop is its own culture," I said.

He said, "It's about spreading the truth versus perpetuating myths. It's not about acting black. It's all different nationalities and age groups. It's a lot of different people. Humans are all made up of the same vibrations, and hip-hop proves that."

My eyes were opening wide. This information was of total interest. When Leo's friend, DJ Coop D'Ville, visited Madonna's one afternoon, I had a conversation about hip-hop with him. This was an astonishing learning experience.

"The mass appeal of hip-hop comes from the ability to report on the current conditions, like gangster rappers, or to dream and talk about the future, as a lot of other rappers like Guru do."

"So what you are saying is hip-hop is about criticizing society and looking for new ways. So all the dancers here are hip-hop as well, because they are challenging the status quo that says nudity is bad."

He said, "Yes, and hip-hop is also about survival, and many of these girls dance to survive. You could easily go and get a job somewhere for minimum wages, but you come here and take off your clothes and get to make a lot more money than most women out there. It's like the rappers make more money than a car mechanic or an accountant. That's hip-hop."

A few days after I met Coop D'Ville, a brilliant idea began to play in my mind: I could produce hip-hop and Leo and Coop could help.

Miami was famous for its world-class recording studios and artists like Gloria Estefan; and the fab Bee Gees lived and worked there. So why didn't more rap stars come from there?

As far as I knew, Miami had only one known hip-hop recording star, Luther Campbell and 2Live Crew. But I was sure I could find a rapper who had something to rap about other than the size of a woman's butt.

Coop was right. I was making more money than most women, but I honestly didn't want to end up like the people in South Beach who go to clubs every night, wear new outfits, and talk about the celebrities they saw.

I realized that I would feel happier learning about recording studios and the music business. I don't care about famous people. I could be a famous producer myself. What did Diddy have that I didn't – except maybe for the cool name? Groupies could talk about seeing me.

I called Coop D'ville and Leo; they both liked my idea of producing a local rapper. They said I needed to book studio time. They would love to come and help me produce, they both agreed. Now, I was determined to find a rapper.

For several months, I frequented hip-hop clubs every night, even after work at Club Madonna.

Do you know what's really great about being a producer? You can go to clubs, but because you are there to find a rapper, you are not wasting your time like all the other people who go there night after night with nothing to do but hang out.

Leo and Coop introduced me to many DJs and emcees on the Miami scene.

Who would have thought that there was so much untapped talent here? Out of every rapper I met, my two favorites were the Foreign Minister and the Al Chemist, two young Puerto Ricans. Their group was called The Chosen Few. They were both former graffiti artists.

I called South Beach Studios on Collins Avenue and learned that the rate for renting the studio was $3,000 per day, which was too much even for a stripper like me.

If I was serious about becoming a producer, I needed to find an alternative. A few weeks later, straight out-of-the-blue, I found the solution for my problem right there at Club Madonna. It was a brilliant Saturday night, with the club filling up and the girls making tons of money. I had dressed in a long, black lace gown with slits on the sides, which was notably see-through; it was like wearing nothing at all, but better.

A man with dark hair and a goatee, dressed in black jeans and a black T-shirt (unlike most people in South Beach), was sitting by the stage tipping me handsomely while I performed. After my set, I joined him. He said his name was Mike.

I thought there was something artsy about him, but not in a flamboyant way. I just couldn't put my finger on it. He bought me a cappuccino and we made small talk.

Mike said he worked at Criteria Studios in North Miami, the biggest and most famous of all Miami studios. Instead of making my rounds, talking to all the customers at the club, and giving lap dances, I decided to sit and talk with Mike. He seemed sweet and a little bit shy, and because it was his first time in the club, I wanted to help him relax and have a good time.

The only thing was, since most men attend dance clubs to get as close to the girls as they can, I just couldn't resist asking him if he wanted me to give him a lap dance. Of course, he could say no if he so desired and I would still hang out and talk to him, because I really thought he was interesting. Sometimes just talking gets too boring and a lap dance is a good way to mix things up a bit, isn't it?

Mike agreed, and we went upstairs to the lap dancing area of the club. This lounge was expensively furnished with gray upholstered chairs and black sturdy tables in front of them that girls could stand on and strip down to their thongs before climbing up on a man's lap.

Mike appeared to have little experience with ordinary women, and even less with strippers.

"Sit in the chair and relax. I'll do the rest," I told him.

He did as I asked. I climbed on the little table and slowly began to dance for him. As I moved with the music, my body seemed to take over and shut my mind to all else.

I moved my fingers slowly over my face, arms, and neck. I began to lower the straps of my gown, showing Mike my firm breasts. I opened my eyes and let the thin lace fall from by body. I smiled at the look on his face as I inched closer to him, trying to be as sexy as possible.

Mike was captivated. I could clearly see his erect member though his jeans. I sat on his crotch and started to move back and forth rhythmically. Mike was enjoying it, but he still seemed shy and kept his distance even as I was grinding into his crotch. I think he was embarrassed.

A great way to break the ice with someone who is so shy they can't relax is to talk about something that isn't sexual. I decided to tell him about The Chosen Few.

"Mike, would you like to give me a tour of Criteria Studios some time if I give you my telephone number? I've been dying to meet a recording engineer. I want to know everything there is to know about recording because I'm getting into the rap business," I said, enthusiastically.

"Actually, I'm not an engineer. I'm just the studio electrician. Do you rap?"

"Do I look like a rapper, Mike? I don't want to rap. I want to produce. The Chosen Few are really good. They're from Miami. I used to take pictures of musicians in New York, and I've been in recording studios, but I need someone to show me about all the different consoles and mixing gear. All people talk about in South Beach is hip-hop and how awesome it is, but nobody produces any local artists. What do you say?"

"Sounds like a great idea," said Mike.

"So you'll do it? Oh, I'm so happy," I said, and kissed him on the cheek. The song had ended and we went back downstairs and watched Grace on the main stage. She winked at us. She could tell that I enjoyed talking to Mike and that I wasn't trying to get his money.

All I could think about was how soon I would visit Criteria Studios, which was much grander than D&D Studios in New York, or South Beach Studios, or Gloria Estefan's Crescent Moon Studios. I immediately told Leo I'd met someone from Criteria Studios. He was beside himself with excitement.

"Are you kidding? That's not a recording studio; that's Mecca. The Bee Gee's recorded *Saturday Night Fever* there," he yelled. "And Gloria Estefan, Aerosmith, the Eagles, Eric Clapton, you name it; everyone who is anyone in music has recorded there. If you get me into Criteria, I'll do anything you want."

"Hey Leo," I said, really getting down to business.

"Yes?"

"We have to get with Coop and the Chosen Few and decide which song to record."

"Yeah, right. We'll meet at my place. I will call Coop and ask him to bring the guys. Tomorrow, before work. Three o'clock?"

Mike called me the following Saturday morning and said he was going to drop off something at Criteria; if I wanted to see the studio, I could come.

"Mike, I want you to help me produce this hip-hop track with the Chosen Few," I said, as we drove up to North Miami.

"What do you want me to do?" he asked, engrossed.

"I want you to engineer. You are the guy who wired the entire studio. You know the recording equipment better than anyone. Right?"

"I suppose so. I can try."

"Do you get an employee discount for using the studio?"

"I don't know. I'll have to ask Trevor. He's the studio manager."

Mike called me later that week with exciting news. He'd gone out for sushi with Trevor and told him about The Chosen Few. Trevor offered to let us use the studio for free providing that we used a room that wasn't booked by anybody else. Also, he asked Mike to supervise the recording session.

Coop D'ville thought it would take no more than twelve hours in the studio to record one song and another twelve hours to mix it.

We decided to record *Paint It Black*, a classic Rolling Stones piece. We'd do it as a rap song with different lyrics – lyrics written by Al Chemist and Foreign Minister.

I had always liked the '60s song because of its exotic far-eastern flair. So, being that the Chosen Few were former graffiti artists, I thought it fit in really well with their image. On the other hand, a lot of people who were unfamiliar with hip-hop, just like I had been, would recognize the Stones classic. Certainly all those dedicated rock fans would listen to the message in the new song with the new sound.

Later that year, when we were finally ready to produce and went into the studio, it took exactly twenty-four hours to record the song, and twenty-four hours to mix. But everyone was excited and tireless; it wasn't like work at all. We all smoked blunts, even Mike, and then ordered delicious pastrami sandwiches from the nearby deli.

Mike, Coop D'Ville, Leo, and I watched The Chosen Few rap from our seats behind the recording console. They were so awesome behind glass with their baseball caps turned backwards and the big headphones covering their ears.

And when they listened to the playback, they stood with arms folded tightly and heads bent downward in deep concentration. You know, they were every bit the devoted rap stars I had hoped for when I had decided to produce the record.

The new lyrics of the old Stones hit went like this:

I look inside myself;
I see my heart is black.
Until my darkness goes
My soul can't come back.
I see people turn their heads,
Quickly look away.
Like a new-born baby,
It just happens every day.
Flashbacks, photographic memories
The illest scenery pierced in my cornea
Until I can't see anymore.
Rumors of war, spreading like epidemics,
I can't let it infiltrate
My mind's state remains pure.
The weed is my only cure for this,
Heartless abyss.
Exterior aerosol assaulter,
Roam the late night with a marker
Like a stalker, behind the bushes
Through the mist approach the darkest hour
The fog lifts
No runs, no drips, no errors
When I squeeze tips.
I'm well equipped
Fully armed no way to detect
When I go bomb
Dressed in jet black gear
Only a percentage of my image is clear.

Coup D'ville and Leo experimented with the different beats for the song, but I knew there was something missing. I wanted the song to be catchier, like the Stones song was with that spine-tingling guitar intro. We had no instruments other than a drum machine. Coop assured me this was all that we needed.

But I wanted to take a sample of the guitar in the Rolling Stones track and record it over our sound. The only trouble was that the two songs had different speeds and none of us knew how to synchronize the two.

Mike was tired after being locked in the studio all day and half the night, but some people are even more brilliant when they are tired. He called a young sound engineering student and musician named Alfred who had just recently started an internship at Criteria. Alfred drove over at midnight and listened to our track. Then he listened to the Rolling Stones track. Then he pulled out his guitar and played the notes, but slower.

It worked.

We had done it.

We were all excited, and I don't think I slept for a week afterwards. I was sure hip-hop stations in Miami would immediately play *Paint It Black*. Without delay, I started calling the most important radio DJs in town.

DJ Felix Sama of Power 96 was the first to play the CD. He loved it and asked me when I would have more CDs. I ordered one thousand copies. But when I went to my entertainment lawyer to copyright the song, something completely awful happened.

The lawyer told me that the song didn't belong to the Rolling Stones but to Allen Klein, a nemesis of hip-hop. He said Allen Klein would never give his permission to publish our song if the original lyrics were altered. If I sold the CDs, Klein could sue me for the profits, just as he had sued Method Man, who sampled the Rolling Stones song *Get Off of my Cloud*.

Nightmare!

With this new information, I went to Mike's apartment to hide from Coop and Leo and The Chosen Few. You can imagine how devastated I was. I cried all day with Mike consoling me. He was sweet.

"You'll record other songs. This has been a wonderful education for you. I learned a lot from it myself. It was really fun. Besides, I got to hang out with you."

Oops.

I never thought of Mike in a romantic way. He was more like a smart older brother.

"I would like to see you again," he said.

"Well – " I trailed off. Did I want to see Mike again? I guess I did. He was cool and sweet and wasn't at all into that South Beach club and model scene.

"Maybe," I said.

I was still very upset by my failure as a hip-hop producer. But something positive did come out of producing *Paint It Black*. I had sent a CD to Intune, a brand new local record label in the trendy design district in downtown Miami. After talking to the company owners about my near success as a producer, they offered me a job in their office, even though they knew I worked as a stripper.

It was almost Christmas, and we had agreed that I would start at Intune after the New Year.

Joe Risolia and Jim Walgreen, my new bosses, were innovative guys with a huge budget, courtesy of the Walgreen family fortune. Intune had recently signed a local reggae artist named Raw B.J. and they asked me to come help them with the club and radio promotions.

I agreed.

Then Jim gave me this long article to type and I found myself handcuffed to a pc for one full day. So, I surfed the World Wide Web.

I stumbled upon an article about Aaron Sorkin. I couldn't believe it. It said that Aaron was working in television, as a writer for the sitcom, *Sports Night*, for ABC.

Since I was sitting inside a slick, modern record label, and working for the Walgreen family, I felt compelled to call Aaron in L.A. and tell him where I was. I called ABC Studios and got connected to Aaron immediately.

"Hello, this is Aaron Sorkin," he said, his voice immediately bringing back memories..

"Hi. I don't know if you will remember me. This is Dimitra, from New York."

"How are you?" he answered quickly. It had been almost five years, but he sounded as if we were best friends.

"It's so great to hear from you. Where are you?"

"I am in Miami," I replied. "I am working for a record label. I produced a CD, but I'm not allowed to sell it. It's a long story. How are you?"

"I'm great. I'd like to get your e-mail and write you, if that's okay," he said.

"Okay." I gave him my e-mail address at Intune and hung up. This was so weird, I thought. No way would he e-mail me. But if he did, it would be great for Joe and Jim to know that I knew someone at ABC in L.A. Although I secretly hoped to hear from Aaron, it came as a shock when I received this e-mail from him the next day at work:

From: ASorkin@aol.com

To: Dimitra@Intunerecords.com

Re: How are you?

Dimitra,

I could never forget you. I still think of how you used to hang lingerie from my potted plants in New York. I don't believe I ever found anything sexier in my life. Write me more about what you are doing.

Love, Aaron

I felt paralyzed. I couldn't believe Aaron wanted me to write him. I mean, don't television writers work, like sixteen hours a day? Surely, I thought, Aaron was just being polite. But why had he sent me such a racy e-mail? Could he really still be thinking about me that way?

Anyway, I wanted to ask him to listen to Raw B.J.'s songs, in case he could use them for his TV show. But to ask such a favor seemed too opportunistic.

Knowing that Aaron was still thinking about us in New York, I decided to wait and see what developed with us, e-mail wise. I could always ask him later, I thought. So I wrote back this nice, personal e-mail:

Aaron,

It's nice to hear from you. I remember the times we spend in New York very well. I have to admit something: I always had a crush on you. I am sorry that my boyfriend James called your apartment that one time.

Love, Dimitra

I really *did* have a crush on him back then. But the thing was, I couldn't talk about it or tell him because to do so would have been very unprofessional for a call girl. But there, I had told him now.

137

I waited anxiously for his reply; it came right away. He wrote:

> Dimitra,
>
> I don't remember James calling my apartment. You had a crush on me?

Now the e-mails were coming like clockwork, I would write to him and he would pop a note right back. My job at Intune couldn't have been more exciting. I hurriedly followed up on one e-mail after another.

> Aaron,
>
> Yes, I did. You were so young and smart and cute. I was too intimidated to tell you how I felt.
>
> Love,
>
> Dimitra

Aaron and I continued our correspondence during the rest of my career at Intune and while he continued writing *The West Wing* series.

In the second episode of the show, the character Mandy gets fired from her job as a publicist, and she says, "I can get another job. I'm young and smart, and don't forget how cute I am." I am aware, of course, that my lines in e-mails are not copyrighted; however, I thought the phrases were really close to the e-mail I had written to him less than four weeks prior to the episode.

After our constant e-mailing back and forth, I decided it would be proper to mention the CD I had produced. So I told Aaron about *Paint It Black* and The Chosen Few.

I sent him a videotape of the group performing the song at Club Groove Jet as well as a CD of the song. I asked if he could use the song on television.

When I received his reply, I was excited and grateful. His e-mail said:

Dimitra,

I will take a look at the video. Of course I would do whatever you asked.

It seemed everything was really fine between Aaron and me. I kept e-mailing him, and he kept e-mailing me.

The e-mailing had started in January 1999; now it was getting into October. And little things I said kept popping up now and then on *The West Wing*. I noticed the connection right away.

In the pilot episode, the President of the United States, Martin Sheen, sprained his ankle only three weeks after I had written to him that I had sprained my ankle. Coincidence?

Once *The West Wing* aired, it skyrocketed straight to the top of the charts. I e-mailed Aaron and told him of the Websites dedicated to the show and to him exploding up all over the Internet.

I told him about all the female fans lusting over him. He replied and said that I was the only fan he has ever seen wearing lingerie and that he couldn't wait until I came to L.A. to visit.

He was married then, but I thought I would go visit him anyhow if he used *Paint It Black* in the show. But he never did.

I finally quit work at Intune and Club Madonna and went to the Kit Kat Ranch in Nevada.

Aaron and I continued to send e-mails back and forth. He kept making promises, but I think they were just some of his many words on paper.

Chapter Ten

Many women in L.A. seem to be cautious of having a career. However, there is one career here they seem very enthusiastic about. The most desired occupation here is to work as an actress in film or television.

Inexplicably, most actresses get their start at places like restaurants, coffee shops, or behind the reception desk of the Beverly Hilton Hotel. I can usually tell they are actresses because they typically act as if they abhor their jobs much more than most people. Honestly, the "actress" who checked me into my room would have done anything to meet William Richert, and I probably could have introduced her. She had no idea I would soon meet Bill in that very same hotel.

After glancing at me the way she might have regarded a used napkin, she pronounced my name six different wrong ways and sourly handed me my room key. Still, I was happy to be in L.A. My new career as a writer was imminent.

Controversy was also imminent because of my history with Sorkin. I never denied there was something for me in all that controversy. I was paid for some of the interviews. But I honestly didn't do it for the money. I didn't do it for revenge. I did it for the closure.

And I received more positive than negative responses when I broke all the rules and appeared in *Star* magazine, the *New York Daily News*, and in the other newspapers. Sorkin had his own way of following up on these stories.

He created an episode in *The West Wing*, in which the fictitious Vice President of the United States resigned from office because a woman he'd had an affair with published a book about it. This would be the last episode he wrote for *The West Wing*. Very original.

Shortly after the episode aired, he quit the show as its producer and writer.

To be perfectly honest, I never blamed myself for Aaron leaving television, but a few of the girls at the Kit Kat ranch did. It was like, all they could talk about was that he left NBC because I couldn't keep a secret. They felt sorry for him, the poor rich millionaire; but they didn't seem to feel sorry for me when Aaron used my character in the show.

Even though the Aaron-me thing had happened twelve years prior, it still consumed me. Of course, people can keep secrets a lot longer than twelve years, but going public was like therapy for me. It was the thing that saved me, and so I had to tell William my story.

There was no going back now.

I called Bill as soon as I walked into my room at the Beverly Hilton. "How about lunch at noon tomorrow? Come and have lunch at the Griff's with me," I said.

"That would be great," he replied. "I'm really excited to meet you. Oh, and my wife will join us, if that's all right."

"No problem," I said.

"See you tomorrow," Bill said, and hung up.

I headed for Venice Beach. Smelling the salty air and watching surfers ride the big swells in the Pacific Ocean always relaxes me. There is no better feeling than treading barefoot on fine sand.

After two hours of fooling around in the picturesque California sun, I was as happy as Oprah in a shoe store.

I returned to the Hilton, showered, and looked at myself in the full-length mirror in the bathroom. My legs were still beautiful. Muscular, defined, lean. My butt and abs looked sensational. I think I have pretty lips and eyes, too.

I'm very shy and private, and I had been somewhat apprehensive about Bill videotaping the interview, but looking at myself now I reckoned that I was unquestionably cute, and I didn't have to be alarmed about anything.

The next day I threw on a khaki DKNY mini-skirt and white Bebe halter-top and headed to the restaurant. Bill and his wife were already there. I recognized them immediately.

In a room full of tourists, all wearing identical brightly colored shirts and shorts and white sneakers, Bill and Gretchen looked like Roger Vadim and Brigitte Bardot.

Bill, an unorthodox multi-talented producer-director-screenwriter-actor had made several unexpected and personal films within the Hollywood studio system in the '70s and '80s. And he undeniably had the ethereal grace of artists. He had long, flowing hair and wore jeans and one of those terribly romantic poet or pirate shirts; you know, the kind you see on heroes as they dash about in period films.

Gretchen was a lovely, statuesque blonde and former model. She looked striking in a black T-shirt and khaki shorts.

After our introductions, I sat down and ordered a cappuccino. Bill and Gretchen were already drinking a Chardonnay.

It was very evident to me from the first moment I met him that Bill was not an ordinary movie business-type man.

For a split second, I thought about the brilliant attorney, my client Brian, who had just laughed at Sorkin's behavior. If I'd listened to Brian's advice, I wouldn't even be here right now, I thought.

"Why don't you tell me about your relationship with Sorkin?" Bill began.

"We go way back," I replied, a little embarrassed.

"Listen, you don't have to be shy. You know that I wrote the script for 'The Happy Hooker.' I am the last person on earth to judge you."

"I know," I said. Bill and Gretchen couldn't have been warmer. A week ago, I thought talking about Sorkin in a crowded restaurant would be a nerve-wrecking ordeal. But here and now, I suddenly relaxed.

I forgot about the other people actually within our hearing distance and the camera that was focused on me. I felt as though I was just hanging out with Bill and Gretchen in their own living room. That's the thing about great directors. They are so subtle that you don't even know they are directing at all. I swear Bill made me feel so comfortable while discussing sex and drugs and Aaron. He truly has a hypnotizing quality. He really got right to the heart of the matter without too much prying. I admire that.

Most people I know have to ask a million questions before they even understand small things; it seems they are totally unaware that taking someone's words and ideas and presenting them as their own is an act of plagiarism.

"How did you two meet?" Bill said.

"We met through the escort agency I worked for in New York," I said. "One night he just called and asked for a redhead with beautiful legs. The agency called me, and I went to see him."

"Really?" Bill asked, sitting back in his chair; he never took his eyes off me.

"Yes. I was really blown away by him. He was cute and sweet, and he had that incredible penthouse overlooking all of Manhattan."

I had seen Bill before. I now remembered him. In a film called *My Own Private Idaho*, starring River Phoenix and Keanu Reeves. Bill was a gay hustler and got to kiss Keanu Reeves. River Phoenix played a narcoleptic male prostitute.

My Own Private Idaho was the film that marked River's true emergence as the James Dean of his generation.

The movie was of course much too edgy to be nominated for an Oscar, but the performances by the actors were beyond anything any award could ever offer.

Bill, River, and Keanu starred as three modernized versions of Hal, Poins, and Falstaff from William Shakespeare's play *Henry IV*. Even some of the dialogue was derived from the play. Here is part of the first speech that Shakespeare gives to Hal:

"Unless hours were cups of sack, dials the signs of leaping houses, and the blessed sun himself a fair hot wench in flame-colored taffeta" transformed into "Unless hours were lines of coke, dials looked like the signs of gay bars, or time itself was a fair hustler in black leather..."

The film was set in 1990 and evoked Shakespeare's play not only by such dialogue but also by vaguely Elizabethan garb for some of the street people and Elizabethan-sounding music.

I also remembered that as a director Bill was acclaimed for his rambunctious comedy *A Night In The Life Of Jimmy Reardon* based on his autobiographical novel. River Phoenix starred as the irrepressible Jimmy Reardon, ready for anything but too young to consider the consequences. I remember this 1988 movie so well because I was transfixed on River Phoenix, as were many others.

Over the next three hours I revealed to Bill the details of my relationship with Aaron. I talked about the money, the drugs, and the long nights of playing fantasy sex games. I told him about the years we had e-mailed each other and about the promises Sorkin had made. I also talked about the disappointments that consequently followed.

It was clear to me that Aaron was ashamed to be associated with me, though he had assured me for many years that he wasn't embarrassed for people to know how we met.

I only learned how he really felt when he ignored my wish that my friend Amber and I be extras in *The West Wing*.

But this was nothing compared with the nightmare Bill must have lived through when Aaron claimed to be the original creator and writer of *The American President*. (Bill says Aaron stole his script, he even wrote about it on his Website. I believe every word Bill says because I know Aaron.)

You can learn a lot from a man when you spend nights getting high with him. As I watched Bill during the interview, I wondered how he had managed to survive such deceit.

Can you imagine working on a screenplay for ten years and then someone else reads it and decides that it's his?

During my flight back to Nevada, I thought about Bill's interview with me; I thought about the way Aaron had hurt Bill and me. I found myself wanting more and more for this whole Sorkin-me-thing to go away. I knew that if I thought about Aaron much more I would never be able to trust anyone ever again. I felt as if I never wanted to hear the name Aaron Sorkin again.

It was a relief to get back to Reno. I couldn't wait to pick up my cat and curl up on my sofa with a good book. It must have been noon when I finally reached the Victorian. I fumbled in my bag for my key.

Darn, my key wasn't there. When I reached Henrik's apartment, I put my bag on the floor and knocked on the door.

"Hi!" he said excitedly. "Look who's home, Kenny!"

"Kenny," I called out. He came running to the door and squeaked like a mouse, which he always does when he is really mad at me.

He shot me an angry look that instantly filled me with unbelievable guilt. If there is one thing my cat doesn't like, it's when I abandon him. I gently picked him up and turned to Henrik.

"I can't seem to find my apartment key," I said. "I must have misplaced it." I bent down and emptied my bag on the floor. The contents tumbled out. There was my Mac, an iPod, a swimsuit, bras and thongs, sandals, jeans, T-shirts, and my cosmetics bag. I opened the cosmetics bag. The key wasn't there.

"You have to call the locksmith," said Henrik, concerned.

"I will call Vincent," I said, fumbling with my cell phone.

"Come in," Henrik said. I left my things in the hallway and walked into Henrik's apartment. I dialed Vincent's number from my cell. He picked up.

"Vincent, it's Dimitra. I just got back to Reno and somehow I can't find my apartment key. Could you send Fred to unlock my door?"

"Fred doesn't have keys to the apartments. It is policy that before he enters an apartment he has to clear it with the office. I am the only one with keys. I'll be there shortly."

Eew! Now I had to see Vincent again. After witnessing my mini-breakdown at Reno International Airport, surely he would be displeased by me. *I should get my stuff off the floor in the hallway,* I thought.

"Henrik, please watch Kenny. I have to collect my things outside."

I had just finished putting everything back in my bag when I heard a click in the front door. It hadn't even been ten minutes since I had called him. I looked as the door opened. As Vincent came closer, I saw that he had a slightly annoyed look on his face.

His hair was slicked back, and he wore a white shirt and a blue tie. I had probably disturbed him in the middle of a very important business meeting. I didn't want to look at him, but I couldn't stop myself.

Actually, he looked adorable, but I was still embarrassed that he had shown up at the airport like a hero.

I felt my knees weakening, just like they had the first time I saw him in his office.

"Lost your keys in L.A.?" he asked.

"Sorry," I whispered, feeling even worse than I had at the airport when I thought Sorkin would kill me for talking about him on the Internet.

I'm not sure why, but I noticed there was something different about Vincent today. He pulled out his huge key ring, which had dozens of keys on it, and was searching for the right one to my apartment. Henrik popped his head out of the door. "Hello, Vincent? How are you?"

"Great, Henrik. And you?"

"I am well, thank you. It's very nice of you to let the young lady into her apartment."

Vincent smiled and proceeded to unlock my door.

Success.

It really was super-considerate of Vincent to so thoughtfully come over and unlock my door. The only trouble was, I would inevitably think of him again all day, and all that effort of flying to L.A. and meeting Bill to distract myself from Vincent would be wasted.

Vincent had a way of getting into my brain like no other cute guy I had ever met.

Can I tell you a secret? When you are as infatuated as I was, all the trips to L.A. and all the interviews in the world would not distract you. You could fly to Jupiter and you would still think shameless thoughts about your crush.

Some people get under your skin, like ticks, and fester there. That's why you always see pictures of beautiful rich women like Britney Spears or Halle Berry with a repulsive guy, and they look so in love and happy; and all you can think about is that the guy looks like an ass. If you have a crush, it is sometimes very hard to get un-crushed.

Maybe if Vincent left quickly, I could get on my computer and watch my interview on WilliamRichert.com. I would have done anything to distract myself, even if only for a few minutes.

"Thank you, Vincent," I said, heading for Kenny and my bag. Vincent didn't move. I tried to go into my apartment without looking at him and close the door behind me as fast as I could, but it was impossible because Vincent followed me into the apartment.

I froze. Suddenly, out of the corner of my eye I glimpsed Vincent looking very bemused.

I tried not to look, I really did, but it happened anyway. And just as I had feared, I got that shameless feeling, that I-want-you-to-rip-my-clothes-off-right-now-and-if-you-don't-I-will-die feeling.

Vincent and I just stood in the hall of my apartment not speaking. Then suddenly I thought I saw him looking at me the same way I was looking at him; I mean, as if he had shameless feelings about me. It must be jetlag, I thought, but I remembered that Reno and L.A. were in the same time zone, so it could not be jetlag.

Kenny jumped from my arms and leaped on the sofa. I leaned against the wall for support because seeing that look on Vincent's face had made my knees positively weak.

"You need a key," Vincent said slowly.

"What?"

"A duplicate," he said, holding up his key chain.

"Oh, yeah. Right," I said.

He moved closer and leaned on the wall next to me. I could feel him standing there, but I couldn't turn to face him. It was too dangerous.

If I were going to do anything remotely shameless with Vincent, I would first have to tell him about my being a call girl. There is nothing I hate more than lies and deceit. After my disaster with James so many years before, I told every man I had sex with the truth.

148

Honestly, none of them minded very much. It's just that it is important for me to be honest. But what if I was honest with Vincent and he got angry with me for lying about my profession?

"Would you like me to make a duplicate and drop it off later?" I heard Vincent say. I turned and faced him. "It's not too much trouble?" I said, weakly. Suddenly he stood in front of me. His face was only inches from mine. I felt his hand on my hand. He leaned closer.

"Of course it's too much trouble," he whispered into my ear.

"Really?" I stuttered.

"Yes. You are trouble. I knew that from the absolute minute of meeting you. That's the thing about you that drives me crazy."

"It is?"

"Yes," he said, turning slightly to wrap his arm around my waist.

"Is it hot in here or is it just me?" I said.

"It must be you," he said, grinning.

What was I going to do? Should I tell him I was a call girl and ruin my chances of some shameless activity, or should I wait and tell him afterwards?

I felt the endorphins rushing down my spine. Vincent leaned down and went straight for my lips. With my body melting into his five-nine frame, I felt so much shorter than five-three. Vincent pressed me against the wall and placed his thigh between mine. I didn't know if I was going to fall down from the sweetness.

Actually kissing Vincent made it impossible to think because when you kiss really professionally, you don't have any oxygen going to your brain for two minutes and the brain just shuts down. His lips were so delicious that I didn't notice at all that his hand was under my shirt.

I suddenly felt his fingers gently pinching my nipples. I felt his erection pressing against me. Vincent didn't bother to unbutton my shirt or unzip my skirt. He just ran his hands under the fabric and over my body, which is a thousand times sexier than being naked.

149

He pulled my skirt up, and leaning his body against mine, he began to explore the wetness between my legs.

I gasped. He pulled my skirt up around my waist.

"Vincent, make love to me."

I couldn't wait another minute.

Chapter Eleven

I knew I had not imagined my Vincent-epiphany when I suddenly found myself turning down money for absolutely no good reason. A few days after screwing my landlord, I was getting ready to pay a visit to the Kit Kat ranch when Jake called. (The Kit Kat ranch is a legal brothel in Moundhouse, near Carson City, Nevada.)

The Kit Kat ranch had become my home after I left Club Madonna and Florida.

After Aaron Sorkin had used my character in the popular *The West Wing* series, I suddenly became very famous at Club Madonna. All the other dancers thought being the inspiration for a television character was the best possible thing that could happen to a woman. But for me, the popularity and attention soon became completely draining. Of course, I didn't dare tell my co-workers this because I didn't want to appear ungrateful.

I ended up quitting the job at Madonna's and, after eight years, returned to being a call girl. I left Miami and headed for the Kit Kat Ranch in Nevada – Nevada being the only state in the country that has legalized prostitution and ranches with girls in them.

This would be my first visit to the Kit Kat ranch since I later left there to become an independent escort.

When Jake called, he had barely said hello when I informed him that I was retired from being a call girl.

"I am going over to Carson City to put the final touches on my book," I said.

Four hundred dollars would not console me after the last few days. Four thousand dollars would not console me! Actually, meeting Bill Richert had changed everything.

I had new desires and my life had new meaning.

"Dimitra, please! You can see me, and afterwards I will drive you to the ranch. Saves you at least fifty dollars in cab fare," Jake said, trying to persuade me.

"You don't understand, Jake. I can't. It has to end sometime. I really should be doing something else. Don't you want me to be happy?" I said.

"Come on, one day is not going to make a difference."

"I am serious, Jake. The interview is already on the Internet. I am thinking of moving to L.A. where people are more interested in my book than in my body. Don't worry, you will find another petite redhead. I know we are your favorite," I joked.

"You would rather sit chained to a computer all day writing than have sex for money?" Jake said.

Of course, most men would prefer screwing for money to any other type of career, I thought. Maybe women, too; we just don't like to admit it in public.

"It's just better if I focus on one thing at a time," I replied, bothered. I'm a successful call girl, I thought. I can be a successful author if I wanted to be.

"Being handcuffed to a computer isn't the end of the world," I explained to him.

"I understand. I'll miss you. Call me if you un-retire?"

"I will," I said, and hung up the phone. Even I was shocked by how easy it was to quit. I mean, being a call girl didn't seem to be nearly as addictive as cigarettes.

Regardless of the exciting interview with Bill and my new direction in life, Vincent was still in my mind and nearly within my reach. My phone had been ringing non-stop since I had retuned from L.A., but I wasn't returning anyone's calls. I had not heard from Vincent since the day I'd returned from California; this was terribly embarrassing. If he didn't care to call me, I didn't care to call him.

Nevertheless, I couldn't help but wonder how he could just disappear after the best sex of my life. I tried not to take it personally. The fact was, I was probably only madly in love with Vincent because he hadn't pursued me. Did this mean I was sick?

I knew my visit to the Kit Kat ranch to take notes for my book would take my mind off Vincent. I could visit Lucy and Danielle. The three of us had gotten along well during my stays at the ranch. I dialed Lucy's cell phone and made plans.

"Okay, Dude. See you later," Lucy said.

"Right. And tell Danielle I'm coming."

"Okay," she said.

However fierce my attraction to Vincent was, I couldn't let it interfere with my future. That would be too silly. I had behaved recklessly that shameless day with Vincent. I had been driven by immaturity and a complete lack of recent orgasms.

Now I had to pay for it. I had screwed a man I was very infatuated with, and I hadn't told him I was a call girl; in my world, these are two things that historically only end badly. Then he had instantly vanished into thin air.

As I anticipated the drive to Moundhouse, I resolved to be satisfied about what I had, rather than be depressed about what I didn't have. I still had my good looks, my body, my apartment, Kenny, and my mind. I was an intelligent woman. I wasn't planning on showing up at the ranch looking as crushed as I felt inside.

Look at Drew Barrymore; she gets more successful with each divorce. She always makes these insanely popular movies right in the middle of a marital crisis. Inspired by her, I put on jeans and a T-shirt accessorized with sneakers and glasses; I thought the look exuded fashionable Drew-ish intellect.

As I sat in the back seat of the taxi and looked out of the window, I marveled at the picturesque desert and the colorful hue where the sky met the terrain. The mountainous desert looked as powerfully beautiful in the sunset as ever.

By six o'clock that evening, I arrived at the ranch. A neon sign said WORLD FAMOUS KIT KAT RANCH.

The ranch itself consists of four trailers. A ten-foot white-iron fence surrounds the buildings. The place has been painted several different colors since I had first arrived there in July 2000. Right now, it was fire engine red. Apprehensively, I got out of the cab and paid the driver, then I walked to the white metal gate and rang the bell.

When I was a dancer in South Beach, Sidney had told me about the ranches in Nevada. Sidney, a former porno star, had gotten special treatment working at the ranch, something ordinary call girls don't get. Porno stars get the biggest and best rooms, the most flexible work schedule, and rides to town in the company limo whenever they desire.

The rest of the girls have to work a minimum of sixty hours a week and live in closet-sized rooms.

The gate opened and I entered. I saw a couple of unfamiliar girls sitting in the parlor (that is where girls sit and wait until a customer enters and chooses one).

I wondered how long these girls had been at the ranch and how long they would stay. Some of the girls at the ranch were as transient as the people on the Palestinian border. I sat at the bar near the parlor. Where were Lucy and Danielle?

I looked around just as Sara came from the kitchen, a big grin on her face. "Heeyy!" she yelled, before running to hug me.

"Hey, Sara," I said. "Thank God you're still here."

"Yeah. I have to pay for my son's school. You know how these colleges are." Sara was the single mother of a twenty-year-old.

I ordered a Red Bull with Absolut vodka and went to feed the jukebox. One of the girls sitting on the red sofa in the parlor came to the bar. She wore a blue satin slip-dress and blue platform stiletto heels. She was very young, and still had baby fat. Maybe she was eighteen. She ordered a drink.

"Where are the guys?" I asked Sara. "This is so quiet."

"It's still early. You know we don't usually get busy until eight or nine. You used to work nights, didn't you?" said Sara.

"Yes. Ten to ten."

The girl in the blue dress had probably worked all night and was waiting for her shift to end before she could go to her room to sleep. I had been at the ranch only a few minutes when I heard the sound of an engine. A black SUV was approaching the parking lot. I recognized the man driving.

Maybe I should have dressed up a bit, I thought, as I watched Jason getting out of the vehicle and pushing the gate buzzer. As he approached the bar, I tried to act super-cool.

Jason was the only man I had met at the ranch with whom I'd had sex for free several times (except the first time, when he actually paid me). He wasn't even a client. Tall, handsome, and super-athletic, he was a professional Major League baseball player.

He sat down next to me at the bar. As he kissed me on the cheek, his hand went straight to my ass. I noticed that his dark hair was longer than usual, and he had a new goatee a la Chris Cornell. He looked as shamelessly delicious as ever.

"Nice to see you," he said.

Sara flew out of the kitchen to fetch Jason a Budweiser, the way all the staff at the ranch always fawned over him. Women go totally mental when he enters a room.

Even the girl on the couch was suddenly wide-awake and staring at him as if she had just seen a man for the first time in her life.

"How are you?" I said, smiling and looking him right in the face.

"Good. And you?" he said.

I knew I shouldn't have seduced Jason every time he came over to fix the jukebox because Frank, the Kit Kat's owner, had told all the girls that Jason was off-limits.

Frank and Jason's dad were old friends, and Frank didn't want Jason to get addicted to the girls in the brothel like so many men get addicted. To Frank's credit, he is the only brothel owner I ever heard of who didn't sleep with any of the girls there, and neither did any of his staff.

"Visiting?" Jason asked.

I adore Chris Cornell-type men. "I came to visit Lucy and Danielle. I think they are still sleeping," I said.

"What do you do for work now?" he asked.

"Nothing. I want to be a full-time writer. I am moving to L.A.," I said.

"Sounds exciting. From what I have read, I think your writing is phenomenal," he said, grinning at me.

"Thank you," I said.

No man had ever arrested my attention the way Jason did when I first saw him. At the time, I didn't know who he was. Honestly!

He had been at Frank's birthday party at the ranch, dressed in Armani and never in a million years expected to have sex with a pro.

It was his first time at a brothel, but the instant I saw him I went over to him and told him he was one of the hottest men I had ever met. We were standing at the crowded bar sipping champagne, flirting, and the sparks flying between us were almost visible.

I felt Jason's erection pushing against me; his hand was wrapped around my waist.

It was easy to get him to give me his credit card, which I gave to the cashier before taking Jason by the hand and leading him to my room. (The thing is, when you are wearing a sheer white negligee and five-inch stilettos and you have to walk very, very slowly in those shoes because you don't want to fall down and break something; it inevitably drives the man who's walking close behind you crazy with lust.)

I knew the hallway at the ranch was barely wide enough for one person because, as I mentioned, it was just a trailer and not really a house. But the narrow space was really convenient because Jason had to walk a few steps behind me, watching my thong-clad ass until we reached my room at the end of the hall.

As soon as we reached my room, we tore each other's clothes off and Jason kissed me for an hour in ten different regions.

Afterwards, we lit a joint and smoked it, blowing the smoke out of the window so Frank, who's office was only a few feet away, wouldn't smell it.

It was such a turn-on to have sex with the only man I had been told not to touch, and I really didn't care who knew it. Everyone had seen us walking to my room and not returning for two hours.

The cashier immediately told Frank that his friend's son was in my room doing shameless things for money; but Frank couldn't do anything about it because Jason was a grown man, not a little boy, and when a man wants to sleep with someone, another man respects his wish.

A few girls who had tried unsuccessfully to hook up with Jason were beyond angry with me and stopped talking to me for the rest of my stay at the ranch. Misty even threatened to kill me.

So, it just happened that suddenly the boring life at the ranch wasn't so boring anymore.

Jason had no idea you could work in a brothel, have sex for money, and be so jaded that you have to smoke weed or drink alcohol every day just for entertainment. Most men can't understand how tedious brothels are. Sex for money can be completely and utterly boring.

Finally, Danielle appeared, thus relieving me of all those memories. She was made up beyond belief in a long black dress that accentuated her pretty curves. Her waist-long chestnut hair was blown straight and glimmered in the colored light of the bar. She hugged and kissed me on the cheek and ordered tequila and a Corona. Danielle is very proud of her Mexican heritage, although she was born in San Francisco and raised by her American mother. Her Mexican dad had vanished before she was born.

For Danielle, drinking and talking to her friends at the bar, with no customers in sight, was about as much fun as she would ever have here.

Danielle hates screwing men for money. She hates when customers in the bar lewdly touch her ass because it looks like JLo's and they say they just can't help themselves. Mostly she hates the men who try to negotiate over the price. It'd degrading. It really is. Some of us don't like it.

I thought I never wanted to set foot in the Kit Kat again after I left. But now, I was glad I had come back, even if only for a short visit to get a new feel of the environment for my book. Of course, I didn't tell Danielle or Jason how I felt. Just hanging out drinking with them was fun, and I couldn't spoil the moment. I kept wondering where Lucy was.

I looked back at the young girl in the blue dress just sitting on the couch with a red beaded pillow at her side; she was just waiting for a man to come in and pick her. She looked shy, just like Lucy had been when she first started at Kit Kat at age eighteen. I painfully remembered Lucy.

Despite the fact that Lucy had only slept with one man, her boyfriend Kevin, she eagerly became a working girl. She gave most of her money to her boyfriend who supported his ex-wife and a baby, but I guess she was happy to work at the ranch, get to dress up in sexy outfits every night, smoke blunts, and be chased around by middle-aged guys whom she literally led around by their penises.

She had learned quickly that the harder to get she played, the more they would want her and the more they would be willing to pay. But I couldn't imagine what she wanted with Kevin.

I turned to Sara and asked her to call Lucy's room. Maybe she hadn't heard her wakeup call this evening.

The girls' rooms at the ranch have this brilliant two-way system where you can talk to the cashier in the office through a microphone in the ceiling. It's so that when girls are negotiating the price they don't lie about the amount the customers pay. The house gets fifty percent, but no one would know how much you actually got paid unless someone was listening to every negotiation.

As I sat at the bar making conversation with Danielle and Jason, I thought about the time when Jason and I had sex in my room and I pretended that I was negotiating the price with him. I took him to the bathroom and told him to sit on the toilet seat. He did, and I straddled his lap with the bathroom door closed.

Whoever was listening to the two-way system couldn't hear anything.

I knew the staff would shortly come to the room to check what was going on. This was strictly out of jealousy, of course, though the cashier would pretend it was for security reasons. When they don't hear any negotiating, they assume something terrible is happening, like the customer is murdering the girl.

The cashier in the office knew that Jason wasn't murdering me, but she was so evil she came and knocked on the door anyway.

"Dimitra. Are you okay?"

I had locked the door, which we weren't supposed to do.

"Yeah, fine," I said, moving up and down on Jason's lap. My back was turned to him, so I felt his heavy breathing while he kissed my neck. She knocked again.

"Hang on," I yelled. "I'll be out in a minute."

I did not like the idea of stopping.

We were both drenched in sweat when we emerged five minutes later looking like we were on our honeymoon, or something.

We walked past the little office where the cashier sat listening to a real negotiation over the intercom. She turned to stone when Jason and I passed her office and the only sound she could produce was "tsk, tsk."

No one did anything like firing me of course, because, as you know, Jason was a friend of Frank's family and no one fires girls that family members have sex with.

It was my guess that the cashier really wanted Jason herself. She knew he wouldn't even look at her, so she really didn't want anybody else having the pleasure.

Once a girl becomes a fixture at a brothel, it is hard to return to the outside. Sometimes I wonder if I would have ever left the Kit Kat if it had not been for the boost in self-esteem I'd gotten for defiantly seducing Jason and then flaunting it. It was my first step towards independence from the ranch.

The other girls, except for the jealous ones, worshipped me when word of the fling I was having with Jason got around. I was getting a lot more respect then. The last time I'd seen Jason was two days before I quit the Kit Kat. It was sad telling him I was leaving, but I couldn't wait to work alone, like Amber had done several months earlier.

As I waited for Sara to wake Lucy, I slipped one hand on Jason's thigh, and he instantly turned to face me.

"Sorry, I just couldn't resist," I said. "I needed to find out if our chemistry is still there."

"It was amazing, wasn't it?" he whispered. "I am telling you, I get hard just talking to you."

I jumped off the stool and straightened my clothes. Vincent's face had appeared all of a sudden. I wanted Vincent.

"Oh, hi," came a girlish voice behind me. Lucy had appeared in a jeweled thong and bra and silvery heels. I smiled and hugged her.

"I overslept. I just remembered that you were coming over. How's it going? Have you published your book, yet?"

"Almost," I said. Then, "So, are you still with Kevin?"

"Sure, I love him. I'll never leave him," Lucy said.

"I have to write a little bit about this place, so I thought it might be helpful if I visited," I said.

"Hi, Jason," Lucy said. "How are you, gorgeous?"

"Good, Lucy. How are you?"

"Just chillin'," she replied. "Are you two together or something?" she continued, looking from me to Jason and back again."

"No, silly. Jason doesn't want anything to do with me because he feels women shouldn't go out to L.A. and write controversial book involving crack-smoking television producers. Jason is a good Polish boy who wants his woman at home, raising his children and cooking for him. Right Jason?"

"You're so wrong," Jason said, shaking his head.

"Sorkin," he said, "should have known what he was doing. He has nobody to blame but himself. You are just doing what anyone would do if only they could. The truth is, a lot of women aren't interested in reading and writing, be they working girls or otherwise. I have a lot of respect for you writing about what happened."

"That's the nicest thing you ever said to me, Jason. That, and calling my writing phenomenal," I said. I meant it. "Danielle, can I buy you another drink? I have to go home and finish my story soon," I said.

"Okay, whatever," Danielle replied, disappointed.

"Don't look so upset, Danielle. I will come back, soon. You can visit me in Reno. We can hang out."

This was sad. I'd left some of the nicest, most decent women to pursue my dream.

I wondered what Drew Barrymore would say in this situation.

I thought about the girls and me during the long cab ride back to Reno. Danielle and the other girls had always been just as depressed about working at the ranch as I was, but at least we could whine to each other. No matter how awful things seemed, there were always other girls who felt awful, too, which was very comforting. Whining creates strong bonds. We used to sit and talk and whine all night and have the best time we could.

After I left the ranch and started to work as an independent call girl, and started writing my book, I suddenly didn't have time to whine anymore. And I didn't have anyone to whine to. I had to create the life I wanted, because I had nobody to complain to any longer.

It is so easy to get dependent on cooks and maids, that you inevitably forget that you are an adult who should really take care of yourself and that you are not a helpless child.

I have no objections to cooks and maids per se, but I feel I should only have those luxuries when I don't have to have sex with men for money anymore.

When I said goodbye to Jason and the girls after my very short visit, I felt like crying. Just to really confuse things, I found myself wondering what on earth I would tell Vincent when he discovered my past, which I was sure he eventually would.

There was a tense silence in the taxi when I rode back to Reno. I don't want to be too analytical or anything, but the fact is that I was scared to death Vincent would hate me when he found out.

He worked so hard. Stories I had told to everyone were not really about Hollywood, although they were a little Hollywood-ish because of Aaron and Bill. It was all about me screwing men for money, if I have to be completely honest.

There I was, sulking about missing my friends when Vincent had been working as a realtor and had bought and renovated properties most of his adult life, and I was probably making more money than he with only a fraction of the work. Until now, I had lived better than most people in America.

I had postponed an actual career forever because it had been easier to get anything I wanted by using my body.

Why was I so upset about being a professional writer? Writing is the only thing that makes time stand still, and each moment and each sense is sublime when I am behind my little Mac.

Had I preferred selling my body instead of using my mind? Or had I been lazy? Both thoughts were slightly mortifying.

I suddenly remembered the joints in my refrigerator. All I wanted to do was get home, get high, and watch television. *Oh God,* I thought, as the taxi pulled up to the curb and I got out. *I am turning into Virginia.*

I hurried to my apartment and fed Kenny. Then I turned on my computer and watched my interview for the hundredth time. Although I loved looking at myself in the video, I was worried that this might not be a good reason to move to L.A.

I knew it wouldn't be too long before Sorkin would find out that I lived there. We used to be friends. Now, I was talking about smoking crack with him in his penthouse in New York, for the whole world to see on the Internet.

For someone who hadn't smoked weed that evening, as I had earlier planned to do, I was quite paranoid. If I had actually smoked. I would have thought the entire neighborhood was following me, not just Sorkin. Why was I worried about him, anyway? There was a good chance we would never speak to each other again, so why did it matter where I lived?

Maybe I should smoke, I thought. But before I lit up, I heard a child's screams coming from a basement apartment where a young couple, Missy and Eric, lived with their two baby sons. Eric worked as a maintenance man in one of Vincent's other buildings.

Suddenly the atmosphere in my apartment was creepier than that movie, *The Exorcist*. I had to distract myself. I could call Vincent and ask that he check on the screaming downstairs. Maybe I would be in for some more best shameless activity of my life.

I dialed Vincent's number but hung up before he answered. As the minutes ticked by, the screams became increasingly upsetting. I heard the two boys crying at the top of their lungs. Missy's screaming at them was piercing. What could two little boys have done to justify such a violent outburst?

The screaming and wailing continued for over thirty minutes. Unable to contain myself and flushed with anger, I ran through the hall and dashed down the little stairs to Missy's door. I knocked furiously.

"What's going on? Is everything okay in here?"

"Fine. Why?" Missy replied. Both boys were standing next to her in the doorway, tears streaming down their tiny red faces. They had scared looks in their eyes.

"Missy, I have been listening to you yell and scream for the past half hour. Are you sure you're all right?"

"None of your business," she snapped. "You shouldn't stick your nose into other people's lives." She slammed the door shut. I was horrified having to go back and spend the night in my apartment not knowing whether those children would survive through the night.

Chapter Twelve

I went into my apartment and locked the door behind me. What on earth had I done? I suddenly regretted that I had investigated the ferocity. I should have immediately called the police.

Furthermore, since the family had moved into the Victorian, I had heard Missy's shouting on several occasions. I nervously meandered through my apartment and collapsed on the bed. It was useless. Sleep wouldn't come. Incredibly, the downstairs commotion continued. Missy kept screaming, and more and more the piercing cries of the two boys sounded like that of dying animals.

Missy's reaction when I tried talking to her upset me. I sat silently for a moment. I believe helpless children are everybody's responsibility, especially if it appears they are in danger. *I have to call the police,* I concluded.

Facing off with a child abuser after my hopelessly sentimental visit to the Kit Kat ranch made the day long and agonizing. Though being at the ranch undoubtedly could sometimes be mental torture, the girls I met there were the kindest nicest group of women a person could know.

As I sat there in my bed, I thought about a woman I had seen in the foyer soon after the family had moved in. The woman had approached me as I was getting my mail and had identified herself as a Department of Child and Family Services employee. She said she was trying to locate Missy's apartment. I pointed to the little steps next to the mailbox that led down to the basement. Now, I wondered why Child and Family Services had not taken the kids from their mother.

Except for the bloodcurdling noises escaping from the basement apartment, the Victorian was dreadfully quiet tonight. It seemed that the only person who was aware of the turmoil was me – a newly retired call girl.

The agonizing screams continued. I couldn't just lie there. Finally, at nearly 10 p.m., I dialed 411 and asked for the number for child services. The operator referred me to 911, so as advised I called and reported the commotion to the police. They were coming, they assured me.

You know and I know, child abusers are not the kindest people. (I am being as nice as I can.) When I called the police, I knew that I was putting myself out for the wolves. Missy would be mad as hell. Her husband would loathe me and seek revenge. And Vincent might even evict me. The stakes were high, but I just didn't have a choice.

If the police would let me remain anonymous when filing the report, I would have nothing to worry about because I wouldn't be named as the squealer and therefore nobody would take vengeance on me, I theorized.

Somebody knocked on my door.

It must be the cops, I thought, as I peeked into the hallway.

"Hi," I said. I was face-to-face with a couple of men in blue.

"Good evening. Did you call the police?"

"Yes, come in," I replied.

"Okay," one said, as he entered my apartment. The other remained in the hallway. "Tell me what happened." He looked around my living room.

"I heard the most awful screams and kids wailing. I went downstairs to check on them."

"Which door?"

"The basement. Apartment number one," I replied.

"How did you know it was apartment number one?"

"It's the only one with children," I said.

"Did they come to the door?"

"Yes. I asked the woman, Missy, what was going on, and she told me to mind my own business and slammed the door in my face."

"Did you see any kids?" he asked.

"Yes. Their faces were red and they looked scared."

He scribbled something on his pad. "Okay. We're going down to ask her a couple of questions. We'll come back afterwards," he said.

"Sure," I said. "Oh, and officer, I would like to remain anonymous, please. You see, I know that somebody from child services came to visit these kids a week or so ago. I wouldn't feel too comfortable if the parents knew that I called you."

As soon as the cops left, I locked my door, laid on the sofa, and listened to music. This was not a fiasco with which I cared to be involved. But I couldn't just let it be. Somebody had to do something for those kids. Right now, my problems with Aaron and Vincent seemed terribly superficial.

I waited for the longest time for the officers to return to my apartment after the screams and cries finally ceased. I carefully opened my apartment door and peeked into the hallway. It was empty and eerily quiet. I figured Richard, Ken, and Virginia were high.

I sat on the sofa with my computer on my lap for an eternity, but I could not concentrate on my story or anything on the Internet. I just looked at the screen and waited blankly. Then, thankfully, I heard shuffling, shoes clicking, and voices in the hallway. The cops were back. I hurriedly opened the door.

"Kids okay?" I asked.

"The woman said her kids were crying because they'd hurt themselves playing," the officers said.

"I'm sure most mothers scream at the top of their lungs for thirty minutes at kids that hurt themselves," I said. My annoyance showed.

"Are you being sarcastic, Madam?" The officer's voice was overly stern.

"Officer, I wish you'd have heard what I heard."

"We can't do anything unless we hear it when it happens. We asked the kids if she'd hurt them and they said no, so there really isn't anything more we can do."

"Well, it was lovely chatting with you officers. Be safe now," I said, forcing a smile. But inside, as I watched them walk away, I wanted to scream.

For the next couple of hours my whole apartment was like a morgue. I looked out of my bedroom window into the night sky, and I saw a star that looked just like the stars little kids draw.

I sat down at my computer and went right to WilliamRichert.com. He had added a fresh scene from his brand new mob series, *The Vindicator*. I had to check it out.

In this scene, Tony, the under-boss and honor-bearer in one of the oldest Italian families in East L.A., kills his pal Louis. But Tony's real problem is with Sofia, who has fallen hard for him and has the clout to get him. She is the Don's favorite granddaughter.

Louanne Sirota plays the part of Sofia. Louanne was one of Hollywood's most famous and talented child stars. She appeared in *Oh God, Book II* with George Burns when she was only nine years old.

In 1986, she played the part of the hilarious socialite, Suzy Middleberg, in *A Night in the Life of Jimmy Reardon*, opposite River Phoenix. Both Louanne and Bill had been close friends of River.

I couldn't wait until the night was over so I could call Bill and tell him of my plans to move to L.A. But now, it was time to get to work on my Kit Kat story, I thought, going from Bill's website to the Word document containing my notes. I began writing about the notorious place of legal prostitution and the oddball surroundings and the cool girls and the horny men.

Like it or not, it was all part of me, I realized. Then I heard a loud knock at the door.

Why would somebody be at my door this time of night?

"Dimitra!" came a gruff voice from the hallway.

"Are you up?"

"Who's there?" I inquired, without getting up.

"It's Eric," he hollered. Hopefully he had come to thank me for my efforts to prevent serious physical or emotional harm to his children. I begrudgingly opened the door. Eric wouldn't enter. He stood in the door like an oak tree and stared, with knit brows turned upon me. He was frantic. "I just came from work. Missy said the police came and asked my kids questions. Did you call them?"

"Yes, I did," I relented. I didn't want to pretend everything was perfect any longer.

"Why?" he snarled.

"Because it sounded like your kids were being slaughtered, Eric. What would you expect?"

"Dimitra, stop it! Missy would never hurt our children!" His attitude made me very uneasy. I tried to reason with him.

"Really? Is that why they wailed for over thirty minutes?" I said, calmly. "Is that why the child services came looking for your wife last week?"

"I don't believe you!" he snapped, shaking his head profusely. He looked hurt. I had not seen this insecure side of him during our brief encounters. I thought for a second that he might burst out crying. Eric was probably a perfectly decent guy and had no idea his wife was an abusive parent.

"Eric, you have to believe me," I pleaded. "I called the cops because I honestly believed your boys were in danger." I waited for him to say something. Then I said, "Please sit, I will tell you exactly what happened." Eric didn't move. He just stood there, as if he hadn't heard a single word. How could he not have the teensiest idea about Missy? This was insane!

"Eric, I didn't like involving the police, honestly. I didn't want to call them. I didn't know what else to do. God, I felt like a fool." I paused again. "I have to call Vincent."

I grabbed my cell and dialed the number. (It did occur to me that it would have been so much nicer if I had been calling him for some more shameless activity instead of what qualifies as child abuse.)

"Vincent, it's Dimitra. Please talk to Eric. He is furious with me because I called the police on Missy." I kept trying to explain, and now I was getting pretty annoyed. Didn't anybody in the universe give a damn about those children? Was I supposed to just go on about my own business and perhaps read in the newspaper about how Missy had killed her kids? It happens often enough.

"Is Eric with you?" Vincent asked.

"Yes, he's here."

"Tell him to go home, and I will call him. I'll see you later," Vincent said and hung up.

"Go home, Eric. Vincent will call you there." Eric looked bewildered. I almost felt sorry for him. Then, as he was leaving, he turned and completely out of left field said, "Calling the cops was totally inappropriate for a hooker!"

He startled me.

"I am not a hooker!" I burst out.

"You are. Everybody knows but Vincent," he shot back, his eyes piercing mine. "I will tell him!" I stood motionless as I watched him disappear down the hall.

I collected myself and sat down to work on my Kit Kat story. I was just about as annoyed as a girl could be. Maybe Vincent would not even believe what I had told him about Missy after he learned of my profession. I mean, some people really do believe that if you are a call girl, you can't possibly be a decent human being with a conscience and concerns for children. Am I right?

I took a deep breath and tried not to agonize about Vincent. It was almost midnight. No doubt he would soon be knocking on my door knowing that I had lied to him all this time about my occupation.

He would probably evict me – not for calling the police, but for being a call girl. Even worse, he would probably look extremely delicious while doing so.

I looked at Kenny, who was beckoning me from the bed; he was the perfect picture of contentment. I watched him with a smile. His front legs were stretched out as if in a yoga position, and he was completely still, except for his huge green eyes gazing at me. Then my cell rang.

I picked it up. "Hi."

"It's Vincent. What are you doing?" He was already outside my door.

"Nothing," I replied as sweetly as I could.

"Can I come in?"

"Yes."

I went to the door. Vincent was wearing jeans and a black turtleneck sweater. He was hot. I thought I would faint. He looked so good, I forgot all about Eric and the police, I swear. Then I looked at his face, and I saw his tragic expression and it made me sad.

"Vincent, have you talked to Eric?" I didn't know what else to say.

"Yes. He's awfully upset. He has worked for me for many years. He's a good guy. He doesn't know Missy is screwed up."

Did he think that perhaps I regretted having called the police? The thought was ludicrous. I couldn't take it anymore.

"Vincent, I'm not asking for your approval about what I did. I know I did the right thing, and I would do it again. What would you have done?" I burst out. I sat down before he answered. Honestly, my legs felt weaker than angel hair pasta.

Vincent was watching me anxiously. I tensed. This was torture.

"Tell me about your book. What's it about?" he slowly asked.

I couldn't focus on his question at all. "What did Eric say?" I asked, weakly.

It was obvious. Vincent knew that I knew that he knew that I was a call girl. There was a long, awkward silence. *I guess I should tell him now,* I thought.

"Well Vincent . . ." I hesitated, but I couldn't prolong the imminent. "It is a little bit about call girls. Me, to name one," I said, looking down at my bare feet. There, I'd said it.

"Why didn't you tell me?"

"I thought you would be upset and maybe evict me." I tried to smile.

"Don't you think people will find out when you write a book?"

"Yes, probably, but you know, I am really spoiled, and I always get exactly what I want. I don't expect you to understand. I'm okay with that."

Vincent's expression was undesirable. I gazed up at him for a moment.

"It's okay," I said. "I'm moving to L.A., anyway."

"So you're going to just run away? Is that the solution?"

"Somebody wants to talk to me about turning the book into a film, Vincent. I am at the top of my game. You know what Hollywood is like. Obsessed with call girls," I said, matter-of-factly.

Did Vincent look sad now? I couldn't really tell. For so long I had dreaded telling him of my livelihood. I was suddenly very relieved that everything was out.

Vincent came closer. "Why are you so desperate to tell your story?"

"Oh, Vincent, it's not like that." As if he wasn't disapproving of me enough already, now I had to go into the whole Aaron

Sorkin spiel. So I told him everything. How Aaron had stolen Bill's screenplay and, without giving me any credit at all, had used my character as the call girl in *The West Wing*.

"I want to show him for who he is," I said. "And besides that, he had no feelings whatsoever when I told him about my friend, whose life was destroyed forever. Aaron could have helped her by a snap of his fingers, but he really didn't care. He is awful, and I don't care who knows," I added.

"Welcome to reality," said Vincent. "That's what most people are like. They are exactly like him," Vincent said. "I don't know that you should write a book about it."

Suddenly, it seemed I wasn't looking at Vincent anymore. He had transformed into Brian. (Remember the brilliant lawyer who was so patronizing?)

"I will not accept that," I cried, tears rolling down my face. He rushed over and gave me a hug. I guess he was not nearly as angry with me as I had expected. And I loved that.

"Would you like me to stay here tonight?" he said, seemingly concerned.

Yes, I thought. Even if I never saw him again, I wanted him to stay the night.

I nodded, and he kissed me on the lips.

Though I was a little distracted by Vincent kissing me, now, more than ever, I knew I had to move to L.A. It was okay to kiss him this one last time. Surely, I would never see him again after tonight, though I have to admit it would be so nice to have a boyfriend who didn't mind that I was a call girl.

So what if I slept with other men? That is not nearly as unforgivable as a lot of other things, like stealing. I have never hurt anyone. I was also not a child abuser, or drug-dealer, or anything indecent like that.

I am not a leader of a country sending young men and women off to war where they are tortured and killed. Then calling others to take their places in these third-world countries.

I looked at Vincent sitting there beside me looking as cute as ever. Frankly, regardless of my L.A. plans, I just couldn't resist some nightlong adult-only entertainment.

The next morning while Vincent was getting dressed, I watched him from my bed. "Forgive me, Vincent?" I teased.

"Forgiven," he said, with a mischievous look in his eye. He left, and I went back to work on my story.

A regular client of mine called around noon. Jay was a successful software developer, and I had known him for four years. Although he was very wealthy, I wasn't even tempted to come out of retirement for him.

"Come out to dinner with me tonight," he said.

"I can't. I don't work anymore." He was silent.

"Hello?" I said.

"Can you just have dinner, then?" he asked.

I thought for a split second about the times Jay had been in my apartment and had shown me some brilliant features on my Mac. He was very sweet. No one had taught me more about my computer.

How could I refuse dinner?

That evening I felt great going out for sushi at Oceano's, the new twelve million dollar seafood restaurant in the Peppermill casino – especially knowing there would not be any shameless activity with him later.

Jay said he had to fly to India on business the next day. Dot-comers often jet set to India. Perhaps it would be a great country for call girls to work, I thought, as he described Bombay to me.

Oceano's is set in a dramatic undersea environment, with blue-cast mirrors and over two hundred life-size replicas of sharks, manta rays, turtles, whales, and other marine life soaring above. The executive chef, Don Hamilton, is a former professional film and stage actor and graduated from the Culinary Institute of America.

While we waited at the bar for a table to become available, a drunken blonde woman on the barstool left of me started talking to Jay as if I wasn't there. Some one hundred twenty seconds of her head popping in my face was quite enough.

I leaned over and said, "If you don't quit talking to my friend, I will knock you off the stool."

Her face dropped to the floor. Of course, Jay was inconsiderate for acknowledging her. Let me try to explain it better. I can tell you that if you are a call girl and your client pays for your time, he can generally be as rude as he wants. He paid for your company, and it's a smart thing to indulge him.

But when I go to dinner with a client purely out of kindness because he says he wants to be my friend, my rule is that he treats me like his date. That means absolutely no talking to drunken women.

But the blonde had been very pushy, and Jay was only being polite, I guess. Still, he had disrespected me, and suddenly I was sorry I'd agreed to come out with him.

The hostess finally led us to our table. I sat down, exasperated. I'd completely lost my appetite. I was angry with Jay and ready to leave him there and go home.

Suddenly I saw a TV camera and lights being set up in the corner left of us. I was grateful for the distraction. Someone was obviously making a promotional film about Oceano's.

I wondered whether the cameraman had witnessed my earlier outburst at the bar. Maybe I should take my chance and try to find out. In a few weeks, I would be in L.A., so I might as well get used to talking to cameraman-type people. I walked over and introduced myself.

He said his name was Edward.

I told him I was a writer. Edward promptly gave me his cell phone number. He said he worked for a local cable TV production company, and he was waiting for his boss, the producer to arrive. It's funny, but after that, I forgot to ask him if he'd seen anything between the blonde and me. There was the possibility of some excellent contacts regarding my book promotion.

Although Bill knew that I was a call girl, and he didn't mind at all, I thought maybe I shouldn't admit to Edward about my work as a call girl, yet.

I went back to the table and sat down. Our sushi was served, but thanks to the blonde I hadn't knocked off the stool, I still had no appetite. Jay was quiet.

I noticed that Edward let the camera roll the entire time we were in the restaurant. Was he filming the Dot-comer and me as we ate? This was strange, so I decided to stay and see what would develop.

I was contemplating having some tuna when Edward strolled over to our table. He had an embarrassed look on his face. I looked at him expectantly.

"Dimitra, I have to admit something. I'm not a cameraman; I'm a producer. I am shooting a commercial for the casino."

"Oh."

"I'd like to use you in the commercial," he said, handing me his card. "You will get paid."

Maybe this entertainment business was too crazy, I thought, looking at him. Was everybody lying? And here I thought I had to be truthful and honest all the time. Meanwhile, everybody else is telling lies for no apparent reason at all.

"Don't look so sad. You're cute. I had to have you on film," said Edward.

"Really?"

"Yeah, and funny." He winked at me, and I looked at Jay.

The tables had turned and now it was Jay's turn to be pissed. Seriously, a call girl getting more attention than Mr. Dot-Com-Millionaire was too much for him.

I had to laugh. I mean, you can have all the money in the world, all the private jets and the Armani suits and the German cars and the huge mansions, but if you're hung up on accumulating wealth, you're likely to miss the most thrilling and ethereal moments in life. They will go past you. In actual fact, the loveliest and most coveted things cannot be bought. They are completely free.

After admitting to Edward the truth about my call girl book, he assured me he was highly interested in hiring me as a writer for a new documentary for HBO.

Jay looked like a ghost. Edward went on to tell me that he would produce an entire series of documentaries, on women's issues.

Could this get any better? I thought. "Call me tomorrow. We can talk about the documentary," he said.

"What is the documentary about?" I asked.

"What do you want the documentary to be about?" he replied.

"Me?" I said, looking around me in the restaurant, like I had all those years ago in the Falcon jet, when the friendly pilot Pete had asked me if it was okay to take off.

"Yeah," Edward said.

"I think call girls."

Also Available from Andrews UK

Kylie
Naked

by Nigel Goodall

Kylie Naked is the bestselling biography of Kylie Minogue. First published in 2002 to coincide with her massive Fever arena tour of the UK and Europe, the book was the first to tell the story of her well publicised relationships with Michael Hutchence, Jason Donovan and James Gooding. From Neighbours to Stock Aitken and Waterman to her disco revival at the top of the charts, this intimate biography, applauded by Kylie's manager for its accuracy, explores the real woman behind the public image. Drawn from interviews with key players in the industry, Kylie, friends and colleagues, Kylie Naked was the first book to delve into the real Kylie, from her success as a soap star to her assault on the UK charts, and to this day is still regarded as the most authorative and in-depth portait of one of pop music's most private stars.

Also Available from Andrews UK

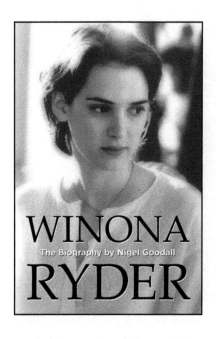

Winona Ryder
The Biography

by Nigel Goodall

Using none of the traditional routes, Winona Ryder established herself as the single most exciting actress of her generation. From her Hollywood movie debut at the age of thirteen to starring alongside Sigourney Weaver in Alien Resurrection, this affectionate biography traces the events and circumstances that shaped her career and propelled her from teen star to cultural icon. This specially prepared digital edition has been completely revised by restoring passages cut out of the original 1998 manuscript together with the addition of new material.

Lightning Source UK Ltd.
Milton Keynes UK
UKHW02061515118
332381UK00010B/860/P